AF239812

# DOLLS OF
# CLAY

DR SHIVNARAYAN J ACHARYA

BlueRose
Publishers

First Published in April 2021

**ISBN: 978-93-5427-735-1**

**BLUEROSE PUBLISHERS**

www.bluerosepublishers.com

info@bluerosepublishers.com

+91 8882 898 898

**Cover Design:**

Joshua feritas

**Typographic Design:**

Ilma Mirza

**Distributed by:** BlueRose, Amazon, Flipkart, Shopclues

# Dolls of Clay

Short Stories, Articles, and Poems

*Dedicated to my First Teachers*
*My beloved mother*

*Smt. Sandhya Rani Acharya*

*and*

*My loving father*

*Shri Jitendra Chandra Acharya*

# Foreword

"Clay says to the potter, today you are kneading me, a day will come when I will knead you"* Sayings of Saint Kabir have always touched my heart.

We are all dolls of clay. Our pride, ego, love, romance, hatred, attachments, anger, property, whatever we hold so dearly to our heart will be of no value to us one day when, within a moment all of a sudden, like a bubble, we shall disappear without leaving any trace of our existence. That moment may show up any time without warning. So, like the dolls that we are, like a mechanical entity, we perform, possibly get praise and claps, and then go in to oblivion.

The artists of my stories are the beings who existed and interacted with me in various stages of my life and had cast their shadows on my thoughts. They all were truly the dolls in the hands of destiny, which appeared and then disappeared from the stage called life. None of them can be described as good, brilliant, or bad. I am blessed that they were in some way associated with me. I loved them, yearned for their long-lasting association but with time I could not hold them, my palms were too tiny to hold them. Few of the dolls were not directly conversant with me, never knew me, but I knew them because of their effect on national or international political scenarios. I have presented them as they were.

In this stage called Life, there is someone raising and dropping the curtain, whose presence can be perceived but cannot be seen. He goes on playing hide and seek with us. We, like dolls, go on running after the mirages of life without realizing the ultimate truth so nicely spelt out by Saint Kabir in just one couplet. *

Now I am handing over these 'Dolls of Clay' to you, dear readers. I hope these dolls of mine will cast their mesmerizing effects on you too.

The Author
Nagpur
Christmas 2020

* माटी कहे कुम्हार से, तू क्या रोंदे मोहे
एक दिन ऐसा आएगा, मैं रोंदूंगी तोहे।

- संत कबीर

Saint Kabir – 15th Century Indian Mystic Saint and Poet

# Acknowledgements

My beloved father Jitendrachandra Acharya and my mother Smt. Sandhya Rani Acharya sowed the seeds of this book. My first teacher, my dearest mother taught me Bengali while she cooked in the kitchen. My father taught me mathematics, history, and literature after he came back from his duty.

I am indebted to my eldest brother, Shankar Acharya, who took me to my municipality school on the very first day, in July 1962.

The 1971 Indo-Pak war had a lasting influence on me, thanks to the war hero Nilkanth, and my *mejda* (second eldest brother) who participated in the war. "Some kind of discipline is a must in life", my *sejda* (third eldest brother) Shivanand inculcated in me. "Life need not be taken too seriously, but a step taken at the right time pays dividends", is the lesson taught to me by my fourth brother, Bholanath.

In all the highs and lows of my life, Debashish, my youngest, dearest brother always accompanied me like a shadow. He and Moushumi, my sister-in-law, shared the assaults of rough tides with me.

My eldest sister Uma is like a twinkling star, who left suddenly for heavenly abode.

My dearest sister Durga shaped my life with love and fights during my childhood. She also took care of my ailing parents with unfathomable dedication.

My life partner Sudeepa, whose company made my journey worthwhile, poured love, love, and love on me. So are my children Ankita and Jaya, who defined their own paths very early in their lives, which assured me of their abilities and strengths. I trust that they will not falter in this stage called Life.

Debts to my teachers can never be repaid especially of Deshmukh Guruji who was my home tutor since my primary school to my final school years. My love for languages was developed by Shri Krishna Kumar Shrivastava who introduced me to Kabir, Rahim, Surdas, Meera bai, Subhadra Kumari Chauhan, Ramdhari Singh Dinkar, and many others.

As I entered the arena of medical school, I was blessed to have teachers like Dr Sharad Deshmukh, Dr Ramesh Mundle, Dr S.M. Patil, Padmashree Dr Bal Swaroop Chaubey, Dr Bulchand, and Padmabhushan Dr M.K. Mani.

While in medical practice, I met a gigantic personality, Dr G.M. Taori whose boundless empathy and selfless service with human touch impressed me a lot.

Newspapers of repute like *The Hitavada*, *Lokmat Times*, *Navbharat*, *Times of India*, *Tarun Bharat*, *Dainik Bhaskar*, and monthly magazine *Sarita* encouraged me by publishing my articles.

My sincere thanks to my kids Jaya and Ankita, my beloved wife Sudeepa, and my friend Aparna Shankaran Mahadevan who helped me in editing.

My sincere thanks to the publisher of this book, *BlueRose Publishers*.

# Content

.

# In This Journey Called Life

# The Nest of Love

Since last few days, a bird was frequenting my home and its mate soon followed. Throughout the day, the couple would chatter and make lovely sounds. The male bird was jet black in colour with a beautiful dark red collar. The female was of a slate colour and slightly smaller in size. They selected a corner in our verandah. Soon they started to build a nest there.

Day and night, they would bring shreds of paper, grass, tiny branches of shrubs, and twine these to make a tiny yet beautiful nest. We eagerly observed the nest grow and soon enough it was ready. It took about 5 days for them to build the nest. However, all of a sudden, the chattering stopped. What could have happened? It was then that we discovered that the female had laid eggs. They were off-white eggs with a brownish tinge. Throughout the day, she would sit on the eggs and incubate them. This she would do for hours together. Sitting like that, she looked bigger than her nest. Her wings barely fit in her home as she sat there waiting patiently.

It became a routine for me to see the birds before going to work. And the first thing I would do after coming back was to peep in and look for any signs of a new born. The days passed by and every day seemed to drag on. I was not able to hide my eagerness anymore.

I wasn't the only one who was excited. My kids were just as eager. The air at home was filled with enthusiasm.

"Papa, what are they doing?", asked my youngest daughter.

"They have built a home, laid the eggs, and soon tiny babies will be born", replied my wife.

"The way we were born?" asked the tiny tot. My wife smiled.

The birds remained silent throughout the period of incubation. There was not a sound. And soon the tiny, little ones were born. They were a featherless bundle of muscle mass, with closed eyes and tiny beaks. We all congratulated each other, as if there was a newborn in our own family.

The mother bird brought feed and fed the newborns. The father bird was always nearby, keeping a close watch.

Often, the kids would be seen alone protruding their beaks, as if they were very hungry. Then, the mother would arrive, carrying some insects for the young ones. They started making noise and the chattering began anew. The hungry kids would shout as if they were demanding food and the mother bird would reply with a call as if to assure them. The moment she would arrive with the food, the chattering and eagerness would increase. They would jostle among each other to get their share.

One day, early in the morning, I got a call from my hospital. It was an emergency. I was asked to rush immediately. I got ready in a huff and rushed to the hospital. As I was nearing the gate, a frail voice called me. I turned around. It was my mother calling me back.

My mother is about to complete her ninth decade. She has tremors in her hands and tongue. She is lean and thin. Her face is full of wrinkles that hold years of wisdom and experience. She contains all the love, affection, and strength I need. For me, she is my home. I have always remained a tiny child for her. She was calling me, asking me to come back.

"Why don't you have some food and then go to the hospital? After all, your return is unpredictable", said my mother with a trembling voice. She had slowly come out of her room, walked with shaky steps up to the door, and then made her way to me. Even in the most urgent situations, I could never say no to her. I turned around and walked to the dining table. She served me breakfast, which I gulped down hurriedly. She looked relieved when I was done with it.

As I started for my hospital, I heard the chattering of the birds again. I looked up at the nest - the mother bird was feeding her babies.

All mothers are same, I realised.

1.02.2010

# Divine Sticks of Mahabaleshwar

**M**ahabaleshwar is a holy place. It is situated in the *Sahyadri* range along the western coast of India. Besides the natural beauty, temples and serpentine rivulets, this place is also famous for its beautifully carved walking-sticks. It is believed that prayers made here always come true. I believe that the sticks from Mahabaleshwar are just as effective as the prayers. Of course, this belief does not come without its reasons.

When I was a child, we used to stay in the railway quarters. Two sisters, along with our parents and we six brothers lived in a quarter, about 600 square feet – courtesy, the South Eastern Railways. I was the seventh child. Our home was always quite a mess and we always had more luggage decorating our hall than required - some useful, many useless, mostly such items which could never be used and yet could not be thrown out. As if the number of kids were not enough, we also had two pet dogs. It was thus not surprising that despite all the efforts my overworked mother put in, the home remained shabby.

My *mejda* (second eldest brother) had brought two walking sticks from Mahabaleshwar. These were well carved with beautifully decorated handles. The grips of the handles were designed to look like the head of a Chinese dragon. *Mejda* bought these sticks for two reasons, one - to decorate the walls of our otherwise shabby home and the other - to be of help to my father who was ageing. Needless to say, the second logic did not amuse my father!

My father was always worried about our future. "Oh! How I wonder if my children will ever become *manush*", he would often say. *Manush* in Bengali means a good human being and *amanush* means a spoilt child. I was his seventh child and far from being a *manush*, I was more of an *amanush*.

Back then, there used to be a mango grove next to our school. During the class hours, instead of concentrating on what the teacher taught my thoughts would hover around the branches of the mango trees. During recess, my friends and I would play hide and seek in this grove. I would rush to the trees and hide among the branches, while my classmates searched for me frantically.

Yet another day, I had spread itching powder all over the benches and desks in the classroom and later when the powder showed its effects, I had a hearty laugh. Then I got a good thrashing from the head teacher. In short, I was a naughty and lazy student.

I never lost the opportunity when it came to any juicy gossip. In fact, I loved it so much, I would listen to other people gossip as well, especially the elders. For them, gossiping seemed to be the only available entertainment, since ours was quite a small town and no cell phones or video games had been discovered then. Needless to say, most of my time was wasted in listening to these useless gossips.

One day, just a month prior to the exams, a family friend visited our house. He started telling stories about some blockbuster Bengali movie he had seen in Calcutta. I was glued to the spot, greedily gulping down his make-belief tale.

My *mejda* was an army man - strict disciplinarian. He disapproved of all this, especially wasting time before the exams. He was home for his annual leave and was watching all that had been going on, silent but disapproving.

Suddenly…

Dham…dhoom…dham…dhoom…crack!

The Mahabaleshwar stick broke on my back. It all happened quickly. Unable to tolerate me wasting precious time, *mejda* had silently brought down one stick and then…

This had two immediate effects. From that day, I stopped wasting my time, especially to gossips. It also

7

made my father very happy. The sticks no longer remained to remind him of his old age.

Many years have passed since then. My father is no more. I do not know whether I have fulfilled my father's dream, of me becoming a *manush*. I often tell my *mejda*, "Brother, your stick has made me a kidney specialist, you should have broken both the sticks on my back, maybe then I could have become a *manush* in the real sense."

After all, the sticks were no ordinary sticks; these were the divine sticks from Mahabaleshwar!


26.01.2002

# The Great Leveler

She is young, fresh, and exciting. She is intriguing! People are trying hard to know her real identity but she remains illusive.

No one really knows her true credentials.

Where did she come from, where is she likely to go, who her ancestors are, what does she look like; everyone is very much fascinated with her but the moment she appears, people just faint.

She is very friendly; she likes to meet people, loves to expand her circle fast, but even before someone realises who she is, she just inundates.

She is a great leveler. For her, everyone is same; whether a person is king or pauper, prime minister's wife, or a simple house wife, she just does not care.

You can be young or old, female, or male, Hindu or Muslim, Sikh or Christian; she does not care. Poor or rich, owner of a seven star hotel or a waiter, white collar professional or a labourer - everyone is the same for her. You could be a master of science or an Illiterate; she simply gives a cold shoulder. Mandir, Masjid, Church, or Gurdwara; she can intrude all these places with equal ease.

Priests, imams, pundits, or devotees; she has dwarfed everyone. She just gobbles up her target without reservation. She does not differentiate between scheduled caste, schedule tribe, Maratha, OBC, or Brahmin. All are same in her eyes.

She pooh-poohs your nationality; whether you are Chinese, Italian, Japanese, American, Korean, or Indian does not matter to her. Your location means nothing to her; whether you are in Rome or Itwari, Paris or Goregaon, New york or Gondia, she does not mind.

This predator is ready to pick up her prey.

She is powerful, extremely powerful, and Single-handedly has brought nations to a standstill. Schools, colleges, malls, movie halls have closed. People are afraid to go out and party, hug, or kiss. Boundaries are closing. No one dares to mess up with her.

She is the frightful devastatingly stunning, beastly, frightful, loathsome CORONA!

Corona represents universal truth. She has shown us that enough is enough, now it's time to behave, remember the good old customs, or just die. No mercy, prayers, donation, bribes, or leniency; she paints a kiss of death.

She ordains us in no uncertain terms that cleanliness is next to godliness. Keep your environment clean. She commands us to have mercy on animals. Don't mercilessly kill animals, have sympathy. She tells us to spend time with our family, play with kids instead of sending them to play zones. Discover the joy of family instead of partying. Slow down. Do not stress. Life still goes on and it's beautiful. If you turn a blind eye to her, she is sure to push you in darkness forever.

Corona, you are novel, novel in many ways. You have broken many myths – myth that man is supreme and invincible. You have grounded not only the flights and wrecked business empires but also the human ego.
Dear Corona, you send shivers down the spine!

5.04.2020

*Background – In 2020, there was a pandemic of Corona virus affecting the whole world with high mortality. Most of the nations clamped lockdown to deal with it.*

# "...Thus, justice is done"

"You have to pay a fine of Rs 500", said the honourable judge.

"*Saheb*, I am not guilty", replied Ramdeen.

"Thousand rupees", the judge ruled.

"*Saheb* please, I am a poor man".

"Thousand five hundred rupees or fifteen days in prison", the honourable judge said as he closed the file and took up another case.

Ramdeen could not pay this amount and hence ended up behind bars for two weeks.

I have known Ramdeen for the last four years. He has been visiting me regularly since his second child suffers from a kidney ailment. This time he came after an unusually long gap. "How is it that you came after such a long time, Ramdeen?" I asked.

"*Saheb*, it's all a game of the stars", he replied. Later he narrated the chain of events that led him behind bars.

Ramdeen used to sell cloth bags at Variety Square, one of the busiest traffic points in the city. This was his only source of income. He was blessed with a daughter. At a very tender age of two, she had developed redness of eyes and gradually lost her vision. Ramdeen took her to some government hospital but this did not bring any results. His second child, a son, had been healthy until suddenly he developed a kidney ailment. I empathised with his story, the tragic tale of his children. I took the opinion of my ophthalmologist colleagues. The girl's blindness was caused due to Vitamin A deficiency, a reversible cause of blindness. But by the time she was examined by my colleagues, her blindness had become irreversible.

Whenever Ramdeen visited me with his son, this blind girl would accompany them, holding their hands. My heart would ache for the poor child.

Frequently, the police would hound Ramdeen for putting up shop at traffic point. Daily they would take bribes from him before letting him do his business. But one evening, he could not bribe the constable on duty and as a result was arrested, produced before the court, and fined. He was told to pay a fine of Rs 500. When Ramdeen tried to explain it to the judge, his penalty was doubled and then tripled. As he was unable to pay penalty, he was put behind bars.

"I have stopped selling cloth bags, saheb", said Ramdeen. "I am working as an attendant in a shop now", he replied. "But why have you given up your business?" I enquired.

"*Saheb*, never before have I been so humiliated. I had never seen prison before. I thought prison is for thugs.

13

For the first two days, even my wife did not know my whereabouts. She was shocked to learn that I was in jail. My neighbours look down on me and my family. Even the neighbourhood children have stopped playing with my kids". His eyes had tears. "I shall never sell bags again; it has robbed me of my pride."

I could sense that Ramdeen had lost confidence in himself. The judgement delivered by the judge had changed his life drastically.

Here stood the man, humiliated and shattered, father of two ailing kids, one of them blind forever. I looked out of the window to hide my tears.

After a few days I happened to pass by the same traffic point where Ramdeen sold his bags. There were a few bag-sellers selling cloth bags. A police constable was standing nearby sharing some tobacco with them, but Ramdeen was not to be seen.

I have not seen him since.

15.10.2001

# Bald Truth

I loved my father very much. He was well-built, hard working, and had a deep voice which made him a good singer. He was a poet, used to penning nice Bengali and English poems. Occasionally, during our school days, he would write Hindi poems for us. He had a towering personality. He was tall, handsome, and bald. His bald forehead added to his personality. During my childhood, I wished to follow in his footsteps. I wanted to be like him.

However, growing up, compared to him, I found myself dwarfed in every aspect.

I am neither well-built, nor hard-working. I do not posses qualities of poetry writing nor can I sing well. However, I did inherit one thing from him – his baldness. As I reached my thirties, I found my lovely dense hair diminish, and gradually it bid me goodbye.

There was an intense struggle on my part to hide this baldness. I started spending more time combing and bringing the remaining hair onto the bald spot in an attempt to cover it. But the mirror always spoke the truth.

It was time I started accepting the truth of my life - *yes, I am bald*.

There are many benefits of being bald. I do not have to spend on hair oil, which is an expensive commodity. I save a lot on shampoo, hair creams, herbal products, etc. As I have very little hair left on my head, I do not have to colour my hair black like my other colleagues do.

If we see the history of the world, most of the great men were bald. The Father of the Nation, our beloved *Mahatma* Gandhi, was bald. Everyone knows of his contribution in the freedom struggle. At the time no one said, 'See *Mahatma*, you are bald!' Instead people fell at his feet, the feet of a great man who we all must realise, was bald.

The Architect of Modern India is Jawaharlal Nehru. He was intelligent, far-sighted, and honest to the core. He steered the destiny of the country, and of course - he *too* was bald.

Netaji Subhash Chandra Bose, a brave leader and President of Indian National Congress, who fooled the English men following his house arrest, whom even Hitler respected for his courage, *too* was bald.

Music maestro S. D. Burman, Naushad, Roshan; directors Hrishikesh Mukherjee, Yash Chopra, Mahesh Bhatt - are all bald. Who can forget versatile Rafi, Talat, Manna, and Mukesh who ruled over the hearts of many? They were great, and *of course*, bald.

Intelligence and baldness go hand in hand, I'm sure. Almost all the noble laureates have a receding hairline!

16

Baldness is a sign of prosperity. Most of the multibillionaires are bald. They have lavish houses, big business empires, and fleets of four-wheelers. I am also thinking of purchasing a second-hand bicycle!

Occasionally baldness may prove too deceptive; income tax department presuming that I must be rich as I am bald, raided-poor fellow like me.

It is a well-known fact that the cause of baldness is male hormone. Those who are sexier are bald. As I remember my bachelorhood days, a rush of adrenaline flows into my veins. My heart gallops fast like a wild horse and my ears become warm. At this point I might end up revealing stories of my good old golden days. I *must not*! Lest this article be read by my beloved wife!

Unlike the general perception, bald men are cool-headed. Shiny bald head reflects light and keeps the head cool while a head full of black hair absorbs light and heat and tends to remain hot.

Besides, this bald head is in direct contact with the environment and hence better ventilated. During rains, a person with a head full of hair is likely to retain moisture and catch a cold but a bald will not.

There are so many advantages to being bald. I feel proud to be an egghead. I no longer feel the need to hide my prestigious bald head with a wig or cap. Nor do I feel an urge to grow vegetation on my unfertile head with chemical or bio fertilisers. After all, baldness is a divine gift, only the fortunate get this boon.

As I was writing this article, my nephew Satyajeet entered my home; he is a young man with dense hair on his head. He was planning to meet his friends. He had parted his hair like John Abraham, today's matinee idol, and has even coloured his hair bronze in the middle. I looked at him wistfully. Alas! If only I could move the hands of the clock backwards again!

18.8.2005

# The Miracle Water

I was in seventh heaven because my patient Ramu had shown remarkable signs of recovery. This 10-year-old lad was admitted in the Intensive Care Unit (ICU) three weeks prior in a state of coma. He had high-grade fever, seizures, bleeding tendency, jaundice, and kidney failure. His father Haridas had brought him to us with great hopes.

In the first week, despite our efforts, Ramu was deteriorating. Devyani, my physician colleague and I were involved in the management of Ramu. As he deteriorated, we scanned many books, literature, medical journals, discussed day & night, and went through the Internet about the disease and the possible treatment options.

In our ICU, we had a very dedicated staff in-charge, Sister Ammini. She was a strict disciplinarian. She meant business with the staff-nurses while being friendly with doctors, sympathetic to the patients, and co-operative with relatives. She was very religious. On entering the ICU, from her face I could understand the status of my patients. If her face is bright, my patients must be improving. Her dark face indicated that something is grossly wrong. A bored face indicated that

19

the number of patients in the ICU is less. In short, her face is the mirror of ICU. If any patient is critically ill, she is in a blue mood.

"Ai ai yo, I shall pray to Jesus for his recovery", said sister Ammini. Her face was dark with pain and anguish because of the suffering child. I appreciated her feelings.

We have a very dependable friend, Jay. I call him a "mobile medical dictionary". He is very intelligent and always helpful. I took his help in patients' management. But despite all our efforts, the patient was not doing well. We had exhausted almost all available medications of our armamentarium. We were feeling helpless against this hopeless situation. The child had started bleeding in his stomach. Lots of blood products were transfused.

I felt as if the earth below my feet was giving way. I was depressed. My enthusiasm had disappeared. I was immensely disturbed with the chain of events. It was difficult for me to face the child's father who was always calm and serene. He had a great faith on us that made me feel even more helpless.

When a patient is critically ill, relatives try to do everything they can. Usually they turn to the God almighty for rescue. Ramu's uncle brought auspicious red thread from a Hanuman temple and tied it on Ramu's wrist. Grandma thought it was an evil eye which had cast ills on her grandson. She brought a

20

black thread and tied it on Ramu's ankle. Haridas ran to the temple of Lord Shriram and brought some ash to smear it on Ramu's forehead. Relatives started reading religious books - Ramcharita Manas and Hunuman Chalisa.

As we were fighting against all hope, the child gradually started improving. His breathing improved. His urination picked up. Jaundice started fading. One fine morning he opened his eyes. A wave of joy spread in our ICU.

"Ai ai yo", giggled sister Ammini. "See sir, our prayers have been answered".

Our efforts were fruitful. The child had started taking feeds. Soon he was sitting with support and began communicating. I felt elated. I was in seventh heaven.

Now I could face Haridas confidently.

"I am glad to inform you that your child is now out of danger. He will soon be discharged. This all was possible because of the continuous day and night care in this hospital and modern-day medications", I said.

"Yes sir, you all have done very hard work but... er...sir, I hid something from you sir", said Haridas. "I have been giving my son the miracle water of a 300-year-old village pond secretly for the last few days and see the result sir, my son has recovered. God has His own ways to make us feel His existence", he said in full faith.

My heaven crashed!

31.07.2005

# Kohinoor

Recently I visited United Kingdom to participate in nephrology conference and had a chance to see *Kohinoor* in the Tower of London. I was dumbfounded with the beauty of it. This large glittering diamond is now glorifying the crown of Her Majesty, the Queen of England.

The authentic history of this jewel begins in the 13th AD when it was reported to be in the possession of the kings of Malwa. It later fell into the hands of Babur, who founded the Mogul dynasty in 1526. It decorated the peacock throne of Jahangir. During the next two centuries this diamond was one of the most prized items in the treasures of the Mogul emperors. In 1739, Nadir Shah of Persia invaded India and all the treasures of the Moguls fell into his hands except the great diamond. Nadir Shah was told by one of the emperor's harem women that the stone was hidden in the emperor's turban. The conqueror then invited the conquered to a feast and offered to exchange turbans as a gesture of friendship. The emperor had no choice but to part with his turban. Later, in the privacy of his tent, Nadir Shah unrolled the turban, the gem fell out and it is supposed that Nadir exclaimed "Koh-i-noor", mountain of light.

The stone continued in the possession of the Persian dynasty, although many attempts were made to gain ownership of it. The Persian king was assassinated and his son Shahrokh was deposed. In an effort to discover the whereabouts of the diamond, Shahrokh's eyes were carved out and boiling pitch was poured on his head but he refused steadfastly to reveal its hiding place. Later, a Persian king fled with it to the Sikh court and Ranjit Singh, the Lion of the Punjab, took the stone and wore it as a decoration. It was later placed in the Lahore treasury.

In the meantime, Englishmen learnt about *Sone ki chidiya*, the golden bird, India and they sailed in search of it till they reached America and then Africa. Ultimately, they reached the west coast of India and took permission of Shah-e-Jahan (in fact from Her Majesty, Noor-e-Jahan, wise queen of Shah-e-Jahan, who virtually ruled over India behind the veils) for trade at Surat and rapidly expanded their influence all over India, taking advantage of the crumbling Mughal Empire.

Englishmen found that India really is very rich in fertile lands, spices, cotton, jute, resham (silk), forests, coal mines, and what not! You name it and you would find it in India. To their great joy, Englishmen found that India is a divided lot, with many kingdoms fighting each other. Englishmen took full advantage of the situation. They had brought gunpowder with them. They sided with one or other king and destroyed both. They found dishonest ministers like Mirjafer who was bribed by Englishmen which led to the defeat of king of Bengal, Siraujudoulla, allowing East India Company to set its feet in India.

After the Sikh wars, Kohinoor was taken over by the East India Company as part of the indemnity levied in 1849 and was subsequently presented to Queen Victoria at a sparkling levee marking the company's 250th anniversary.

The jewel was thought to display insufficient fire. It was decided to recut it from its original Indian form. The cutting took thirty eight days but did not add much to the stone's brilliance. It was rather believed that cutting diminished the historical value of the diamond.

There were three good things that happened because of English rule – firstly, India benefited from the great discoveries that were happening in England those days like the Railways. Secondly, abolishment of the age-old custom of *sati*, wherein women were burnt alive on the pyre of their dead husbands. The last but very significant change was the formation of United States of India. Against the oppressive rule of British Empire, all different states of India united and fought for freedom. In the process we had a single country of varied culture which had never happened in the history of India in the last thousands of years!

As a parting gift, English inflicted India with two deep wounds - they divided India into West Pakistan, and the intellectual capital of India, Bengal, into West Bengal and East Pakistan.

Mother India was gifted with a crown of thorns that continues to bleed relentlessly while our Kohinoor glorifies the crown of Her Majesty, the Queen of England.

15.08.2005

# Hysterical Hindustan

**D**on't worry, be happy *Hindustan*. This is *Hindustan* news channel bringing you the headlines – Aishwarya and Abhishek have gotten engaged. It's time to celebrate, *Hindustan*!

What did you say? Farmers committing suicide...oh, it is a routine affair. It occurs very frequently. It's been happening for over three years now. It will go on happening as the authorities continue to stay in deep slumber. How can it be the prime news? Forget it, now elevate your moods, wipe your tears, it's time to celebrate; Aish and Abhishek are getting married.

Oh no, not again. Why are you in a blue mood over load shedding? You do not get electricity for four hours in your town and for twelve hours in your village. Don't you worry, when our favourite starlets get married, you shall see and enjoy what electricity looks like. The best lighting of the century shall be displayed in their wedding. The world will remember forever the great show! So, worry you not, oh *Hindustan*, forget load shedding, it's time to celebrate; Ash and Abhishek are getting married.

What if the hapless children and innocent girls in Noida were tortured, their bodies dismembered, and their bones thrown into garbage? After all, such small incidents of murder do happen on and off. You should not be anguished for such insignificant incidences, elevate your mood, see, Aish and Abhishek are getting married.

Water scarcity! What is that? Everyone knows that during summer you shall be without water and electricity. Why do you worry about such routine things? The authorities will dig the wells once water scarcity starts. The healthcare facilities? Don't you ever say that! We have severe resource crunch for these necessities of life.

Now we bring you a news flash – Aish will be wearing *anmol Benarashi lehanga* worth two lakh rupees for her wedding. This is only the lehanga, don't ask about the georgette and bandej saris in varied hues of pink, scarlet, mustard, royal blue, and magenta with exquisite pearl and stone work, ornaments, Italian chappals for Aish; designer outfits, and German shoes for Abhishek; Swiss diamond-studded wrist watch for both, and a party to be held in an exclusive yacht over Pacific Ocean where a chartered flight shall ferry the guests. The wedding itself will take place in some palace of Jaipur. Oh, how exciting!

Never mind if the amount spent can feed and rehabilitate the starving hundreds of Melghat forever.

The rapes, day time robberies and murders, inflation, corruption, suicide of Jawans at the frontiers, closure of factories and small scale industries…these can no longer be the headlines. Oh Hindustan, these happen day in and day out. Don't worry and be happy. Aish and Abhishek are getting married. In the meantime we assure you that we shall bring you the latest details from time to time about premarital gossips, shopping, wedding, honeymoon, etc.

15.04.2007

*Background - This article was written before the marriage of starlets of Bollywood. The starlets were leading their own lives. The television channels were neglecting the real issues facing the nation and were full of these absurd stories. Spirit of journalism was lost somewhere!*

*\*The gruesome killings in Noida's Nithari had come to light in 2005-06, where children and women disappeared and later their body parts were found in drains.*

# Just Cool That Heat Off

L ast week all TV channels were agog with the news of a murderous attack by a younger brother on the elder one. From the reports it appeared that the younger sibling thought that the elder one is not giving him an ear, and thereby humiliating him by not listening to him. It appears to be an insignificant event which does not merit a murderous attack. For that matter, any event, whatever may be the intensity of it, does not merit such an attack; but it did happen. In fact, it happens in day-to-day life.

A brother killing brother, son attacking father, wife plotting against husband, and a jealous lover killing his beloved because she did not give an ear to him. What exactly is happening? Why so much intolerance?

When a person is angry, momentarily the faculty of reasoning fails. It is difficult to judge good from bad. If an action is done during a fit of rage, almost always it backfires. This result in loss of peace and respect, creates enmity and low self-esteem. Then whatever a person may try to do to undo that action, he does not recover that respect and dignity again.

Many a times a situation arises when it is difficult to control oneself. My teacher said, "Count to ten, your anger would subside. If you are very, very angry, better count to hundred". What he meant was that one should never take a precipitous action in the fit of anger. Better cool down, relax, and then act if at all you must. One of my acquaintances resigned from the job in a fit of rage only to find that he has landed himself and his family in a financial soup. When I look back, I recollect many events when I expressed my dislikes instantly without giving a thought and almost always, I had to eat a humble pie.

One of the ways to win over an unpleasant situation is to see the events from the opposition's point of view. We tend to judge from only one side of the story while often the opposite side also has some substance. This simulates a situation like that of Dhritarashtra who never saw anything wrong in the actions of his son Duryodhana. Even in our day-to-day life we tend to over-react in a situation which otherwise could have been ignored.

We often form an opinion without judging the circumstances in which an event happens. Once I expressed my displeasure to my daughter for not listening to me. She started weeping with her hands hiding a piece of paper. I snatched the paper from her hand and found it to be a hand made greeting card with the words 'Happy birthday, Papa' written on it. She was busy in drawing the card when I was calling her. She thought that she would surprise me by offering the hand made birthday wish card but instead she got a scolding. I had hurt the innocent child without realizing her sentiments. I took her in my arms with moist eyes.

There are usually three driving forces which make us move. These are - name (or fame), money (or property), and sex. Most of the problems we see around us revolve around these three driving forces. We tend to run after these forces. The craving for these is insatiable. The thirst for these can never be quenched.

Most of the crimes committed are due to one or more of these forces. In today's rat race of life, we have multiplied our possessions but reduced our values. We have reached Moon and Mars but we do not have time to meet our neighbour next door.

We tend to be angry when our ego is hurt. We tend to be egoistic if we are empty within. Every time we get angry, we are in fact defeated by ourselves, for it is easy to get angry but difficult not to be! Those who are full of love will always forgive and forget. In the history of mankind, we find that only those are remembered with affection who have sacrificed, be it Jesus, mother Teresa, Gandhi, or Martin Luther King. We would like to forget the likes of Hitler and Saddam.

During my childhood, whenever for some reason I got angry on anyone, my mother would say '*krodhe paap, paape mrityu*' which means, anger begets sin, sin begets death. There are innumerable incidences in history where anger resulted in self-destruction. Whether we

31

talk about the mighty Ravana or Duryodhana, it was anger that eventually annihilated them.

Be a little tolerant, have some patience, sacrifice your ego, extend your hand of love, try to understand others' point of view and if all these do not prevent you from getting angry, keep the gun aside, count to hundred and just cool that heat off!

15.05.2006

*Background - Murder of Mr Pramod Mahajan, Minister in Vajpayee cabinet, by his younger brother in May 2006.*

# God Drinks Milk Again

The Gods have done it again. Last time in 1996, Lord Ganesha was kind enough to drink milk in different places all over India and this time his parents Lord Shiva and Goddess Parvati did so. Never mind, this is all in the family!

Since time immemorial, we've known that the Gods have special liking for milk and milk products. In many temples the paintings and sculptures show lord Krishna drinking milk, curd, and stealing butter.

But the question is whether the idols really drank milk. The students of physics have an easy explanation. The so-called drinking of the milk by idols is actually the phenomenon of capillary action whereby the liquid tends to move up into a capillary. If you dip a biscuit into a cup of tea, tea not only wets the part dipped but wets the part of the biscuit above the level of tea as well.

Whether the Gods drank milk or not, the news-starved television channels were delighted. The mobile companies too had a field day as they minted money through SMS (e.g., whether the idol would drink one ounce of milk or one gallon, send an SMS!)

Offering food to the Gods is symbolic in nature. This is in fact thanking the Supreme Beings for giving us food. The food offered to the idols is not really eaten by the God but by the people who worship Him. In fact the Creator Himself does not need any food, water, or milk. He has created these materials for the living beings in this world.

Over centuries, the idol worship has led to many misgivings. In almost all temples milk, curd, and ghee are poured on the idols as a ritual. Those who do so should think about thousands of mothers and children in the country who go to bed without food. These poor people can only dream about milk. Many children do not know what butter looks like. These costly and high-protein nutritious substances go down the drain in every temple daily.

During the snake festival, *Nagpanchami,* milk is offered to the snakes with the hope of getting blessings. But milk is not a natural food for snakes. In fact, milk is harmful for snakes.

In south India, statue of Mahabali is bathed with tons of milk, curd, and ghee. In the name of worship people do *havan* or *yagna* in which wood, ghee, food, and vegetables etc., are put into the fire. The same philosophy is stretched to the extreme limit in the sacrifice of animals and even humans in the name of pleasing Gods.

People not only offer food or milk but also gold ornaments, diamonds, etc. In fact, daily collection in one of the south Indian temples crosses a crore. There is nothing wrong with faith and beliefs, provided the fruits are utilised for some good cause.

Rabindranath Tagore had penned *'Tomar poojar chhaley, tomay bhuleyi thaki'* which means that in the process of following Your rituals, I forget Your true self. (In the process of rituals, I forget that you are much beyond the stone idols, you are omnipresent and omnipotent). Idol worship was practiced mainly for meditation purposes so that the wandering mind can be controlled and focused. But over a period of time people started identifying the idols with real God, which led to many ill-conceived practices including animal and human sacrifices.

History tells us that Muslim invaders destroyed the Somnath temple 17 times. This temple was rich those days. Temple property was looted and taken out of India. People believed that *Shiva-Lingam*, the idol of Lord Shiva, possessed many powers. They thought that the moment the enemies touch the Lingam, it would burn them into ashes. But it did not happen. The invaders virtually looted everything without any resistance from the devotees. Hindus looked helplessly with hopes that some miracle will save the deity but in vain. They forgot that the God is far beyond the stone idols. He is in our hearts and minds. That is the reason that Swami Vivekananda had said 'Arise, awake, and fear not until the goal is reached. Be strong'.

God is not to be found in temples or palaces. He would be found by the side of the road breaking stone or in the fields growing grains. It is worth searching for Him amongst the downtrodden hapless poor people. If at all you wish to feed Him milk, feed the poor, it shall reach Him automatically. I remember a hymn learnt long back during my school days. It said -

"When I was hungry you gave me to eat.
When I was thirsty you gave me to drink.
Now enter into the home of my Father,
For whatsoever you do for the good of your brothers,
That you do unto me."

22.08.2006

*Background - In the year 1995 and 2006 there was a rumour that the busts of lord Ganesha all over India are drinking milk. People thronged to temples to offer milk to Ganesha.*

# The Value of Sweat

Sanjay was ecstatic, naturally so, because he had earned Rs 210. The sum may appear too small for a person like Sanjay but this money had value – he had earned it after toiling for a whole day sweating out in the workshop for a carpentry job and in the garden watering the plants. This money that he earned in Yerwada Jail as an inmate had more value than just the amount.

His day started quite early – he woke at 5:30 am, exercised, bathed without soap and oil. He had grown a beard as he avoided shaving becausethe barber in the jail shaved all the inmates with a single rusted razor. After all, the jail authorities could not risk handing over razor to individual inmates. Sanjay felt it safer to remain unshaven than to risk shaving with an unhygienic blade. Later, he would have a cup of tea with hard cold bread. He remembered the days when he would never touch bread. He was used to taking jam or jelly with hot toast and egg followed by freshly prepared fruit juice.

After this delicious breakfast of cold bread, he was shown the way to the workshop where he was supposed to work till late noon. He had to work hard lifting the logs of wood and his soft unaccustomed fingers would try to put life into the lifeless wooden blocks.

The worst part of the day was when he had to queue up along with other inmates with an aluminium plate to receive his lunch. It consisted of three large chapattis and vegetable curry. The curry was delicious except for the fact that one had to search for the vegetables inside the curry to know which vegetable curry it was! The same aluminium plate was used for drinking water from an earthen container full of green algae on its surface.

While taking lunch he would remember the days when he used to have four or five course cuisine which included soup, appetiser, salad, main course with Italian pasta, American chicken dish, boiled tomatoes with Greek asparagus, Peshawari kebab and fruit salad with chosen ice cream soaked with Swiss chocolate from a wide range of selection, and of course English tea. But in the jail it was different. He had to wash his own plate to keep it ready for dinner later.

After lunch he was ushered into the workshop again or was asked to work in the vast garden within the jail compound. He liked to water the plants but it was a bit irritating to be supervised by a constable. In the evening, jail authorities allowed the inmates to play some outdoor games like badminton or football. By evening, another humiliating event awaited him – the dinner. Chapattis cooked in the afternoon, which, by this time had become harder, and the same vegetable curry which had become ice-cold.

He remembered his golden old days again. Dinner was something he never had; it was always a cocktail dinner. He used to wonder why people call it cocktail, as there was neither cock nor tail involved in it! Next day, newspapers would carry the events of the cocktail dinner parties with his photograph prominently displayed.

After a court drama Sanjay was granted bail and he went back to Mumbai in a chartered flight. As he flew back in a hired chartered flight which cost him few lakhs, he carried with him a packet containing Rs 210. The amount did not matter to him but it was the sweat associated with this money that mattered the most. After all, he had never had such a salary throughout his life.

Sanjay Dutt has rejoined the film industry now.

15.03.2016

*Background – Sanjay Dutt, Bollywood actor, had served a 42-month jail sentence at Pune's Yerwada jail after he was convicted for illegal possession of weapons in the 1993 Mumbai serial blasts case. He was released on 25th February 2016.*

# Beloved's Departure

She was wearing an aquamarine green outfit - a shade of bluish-green seen at deep sea. She was elegant, bright and sober, well-dressed draped in aquamarine green - the colour I love. Green is soothing to the eyes; it's a serene colour. So it was not unusual for me to fall for her at first sight.

She was my partner for more than eight years. She cannot be forgotten. During all the ups and downs of my life, she was there. Through rains, chilly winters, or scorching heat; she was by my side.

During heavy rains she used to surround me, embrace me, and prevent the rain from touching my body. Oh, how secure I felt!

She was there through scorching heat. She did not allow the rays to touch my face. She used to shower on me a cool breeze. In that cool breeze, my eyes would shut and I would feel like falling into a deep slumber.

During chilly winters, she would give me warmth. In her lap I felt safe. She would keep the chilly wind away.

Whether I was in jolly mood or otherwise, this darling of mine would caress me and cool me down. It was as if

40

she would sing her heart out to me when I was in a blue mood. She was my Love.

The days are not always the same. Human heart must not be trusted. It's the rule of nature to fall for beauty! History shows that even the Gods and rishis have fallen for beauty.

One fine day, I met another beauty; elegant, beautiful, sophisticated, and charming.

My heart dwindled and from that moment, my inclination was towards the new entrant in my life. My Love must have understood this. She must have felt how cruel I had been to her, for I have used her for so many years. During good and bad days, she shared with me all the joys and agony, but now the time had changed. She must have felt it. The night when I had finally decided to leave her forever, I touched her tenderly, kissed her, and embraced her.

"You have been my love for years darling, but you see, my heart is weak and feeble. I am unable to resist the beauty of the new entrant in my life." She possibly understood. She said nothing. But I could feel her silent tears. She did not want to leave me. I had always been gentle and loving towards her. Did she feel cheated? Did she say that a man must not be trusted?

How unfaithful a man could be?!

I handed her over to an unknown person with a broken heart. He took her away from me. I felt a sharp shooting pain in my heart. Then I realised for the first time that I had fallen in her love. But it was too late to withdraw from my commitments to the new beauty. I looked at my Love being towed away and with heavy heart I waved her good bye.

She was my aquamarine green car of last eight years.

15.08.1999

*Article has been written in humour and in no way wishes to denigrate feminism or hurt any sentiments.*

# Aborted Love

I had fallen in love.

She was a beautiful lass in her twenties, fair, and charming. When she talked, stars glittered and a sweet fragrance spread all around. She had doe-like eyes. A sweet smile adored her face. With movements of her head, her earrings would dance. Her wavy hair played hide and seek on her innocent face.

I saw her first in a social gathering during Durga Pooja. I saw her offering prayers to the Goddess. With closed eyes and a calm face, she looked exceptionally beautiful. I thought that I must get acquainted with her. But how do I start? Soon I got an opportunity. She was sitting alone in the *pooja pandal*. Where the heart loves, there the legs walk.

I approached her and asked, "Pinki, when did you come here?"

She said smilingly, "An hour ago, but by the way, I am not Pinki, I am Anju". I knew that she is not Pinki but that was my way of discovering her name!

"Oh, Anju, your face looks so familiar. Do you stay in civil lines?" I must know where she stays.

"I stay in Ramdaspeth", said she and added, "Why don't you just say that you wished to talk to me". We both laughed. We developed a good friendship over a period of time.

Later whenever she met me, my heart would sing a wild song, it would race fast, and my face would turn pink.

She took a keen interest in whatever I did. She had a good sense of humour.

Once with a trembling heart, I proposed her to accompany me for a movie. To my great delight she agreed instantly.

On the D-day, I decided that in order to impress her, I must look smart. I had a clean shave. Looked at the mirror, oh, no, not good enough, I shaved again. I wore my nicest dress, looked at myself thousands of times in the mirror. Do I look presentable? Oh, no, my shirt does not go well with my trousers. I changed the shirt, looked at the mirror, oh no, the shirt is definitely sparkling, but the trousers look a bit dull. Now it was the turn of the trousers to be changed. It went on and on and on. Sometimes I changed the wrist watch, at others the handkerchief; applied a little powder and thought the next moment that it looks little too much and washed it off. My shirt got wet in the process. I had to change the shirt but then the new shirt again did not go well with my trousers!

I had my shoes shined after half an hour spent.

At last, I got ready. I sprayed a little perfume and started for the theatre hall. Am I too early? She will presume that I am too eager to meet her. Oh no, I should reach the hall a little late. In fact, let her wait for me. The thought of her waiting for me gave me a sense of déjà vu.

I still reached the hall a little ahead of time. Soon I saw the sweet thing reaching the hall. She wore a light pink attire – the colour of romance.

'Hello', said she.

'Hi', I replied. 'How is life?' I asked her with full enthusiasm.

But my enthusiasm dampened a little. A boy accompanied her. My heart sank. Who could he be? Love is blind, friendship closes its eyes.

"Meet my fiancée, Arun", she gave a sweet smile and introduced the lad, who I felt was most indecently dressed, his shirt did not match with his trousers, his face was full of unkempt beard, and he wore dirty shoes.

Many are the roads that do not lead to the heart. I felt like I ate a few quinine tablets. My love evaporated into thin air.


14.04.2002

# The Bewitching Dowry

She is very sweet, beautiful, and pretty. With her unkempt hair touching her rosy cheeks and innocent looks, she must be a heartthrob for many youths. So it is natural for anyone to fall in love with her.

First time I saw her was when she was moving around in the Taj corridors at Agra. She was looking at Taj with awe, wondering how anyone could make such a magnificent monument just for love!

Next time I saw this beauty was at Jaipur Palace with a bright *tika* on her forehead on the occasion of *Holi*. She was holding her dear papa's hand.

I saw all these in television of course.

Her name is Chelsea and her father is Bill. As is the case for most fathers, Bill must also be worried about the marriage of his only daughter, the apple of his eyes.

Recently, she has been proposed to. So what if Bill is an ex-president of the United States, he too must have felt relieved to get a marriage proposal for his loving daughter from a distant corner of Kenya. The dowry is also very lucrative, 40 goats and 20 cows!

This reminds me of miss Allis, another beauty from distant Swaziland, whom I happened to meet at Cape Town a couple of years back. Swaziland is a country in Southern Africa bordering South Africa and Mozambique. Being a landlocked country, Swaziland depends on neighbouring South Africa. The King Mswati III, an absolute monarch rules it. The King has 15 wives and 23 children. The King does not know the names of most of his children! I do understand his dilemma – how can one remember the names of so many kids?

King Mswati III is one of the richest men in the world. He is the rich man of a very poor country. He has gifted palaces and costly cars to his wives. The king is mandated to pick a new wife every year from the virgins who partake in traditional annual chastity rite held in the royal palace. He, of course, presents a dowry to the bride's father. No father can possibly resist the temptation of royal dowry and no girl can resist the title of "Her Highness", even though it is only till the King's next birthday when he chooses a new wife. This custom has been going on since many generations. The present King's father had 42 wives.

Swaziland by itself is a very interesting country. Love flows freely here. It is not unnatural then that the incidence of HIV is very high in this poor country.

I felt interested as Allis was also a practicing doctor - a homeopath, in Swaziland. She was about 22 years old, fair beauty, 6'2 tall, and naturally attractive. She had come to South Africa to meet her friend at Cape Town. Her friend's husband was my colleague in Nephrology department at Groote Schuur Hospital. As we were gossiping over tea, she told me how she was proposed by a young man who had offered 6 cows and 10 goats as dowry to her father.

Unlike India, in African tribes, the custom is just opposite. In Swaziland for example, it's the groom who offers dowry to the bride's father. When Allis turned down the proposal, the man commented that she was foolish to refuse such a decent proposal. After all, 6 cows and 10 goats, that's rich dowry for a girl like Allis! In the African continent, only the rich landlords can afford to offer such proposals.

One interesting fact Allis told me was that the present King is very intelligent and handsome. She was also invited to the palace once for the annual reception, but could not be that lucky one to be called "Her Highness".

Another fact she revealed was that the present king is a very caring and health-conscious – all his wives undergo HIV testing annually!

*Background - Written in 2002, after my visit to Cape Town, where I came across a beauty from Swaziland. Bill Clinton had just retired as President of the United States. A person from Kenya offered himself as a groom for Chelsea, daughter of Bill Clinton, and offered 40 goats and 20 cows as dowry, "My daughter is her own person, very independent, so I will convey this very kind offer", said Hillary Clinton.*

*\* The percentage of adults living with HIV in Swaziland was 37 % in 2002.*

15.03.2002

# The Wig

Once upon a time, long-long ago, there lived a beautiful, smart boy bubbling with vitality, with dreamy eyes, always brimming with optimism, one of the most brilliant guys the world had ever seen. Everyone noticed but one thing - the chap had a head full of lovely dense hair. Needless to say, that guy was me!

In rainy days, in heavy downpour, on reaching home from my municipal primary school, my mother would rush to me holding a towel, wiping my head lest I should develop deadly pneumonia. "Why do you have to get drenched in this heavy rain...could you not wait for some time...see you will catch a cold", my mother would say in a worried tone. But I would not listen. Whenever I got a chance, I would always go in the open, underneath the umbrella of the vast blue sky and close my eyes to feel the sound and fury of the rain drenching me head to toe. As my wet clothing clung to me and my wet trousers became heavier, I would spread my arms and try to embrace the vastness of Mother Nature in the small spread of my arms.

My thick, dark soaked hair would cling to my forehead, tickling my cheeks, a sensation I always cherished.

So happy was I, freed, no worries, always play, laugh, run, no earnings, no domestic necessities, no expenses, no paying taxes! But gradually I grew up.

As I would gossip with Monica, she would run her lovely, soft fingers on my head, would caress my hair and as she titillated my scalp, I would sink into a trance of an ageless, timeless vacuum, trying not to return back into the harsh reality of the material world.

Time flew, years passed, lots of water flowed underneath the Howrah bridge and here I am- getting wiser day by day, my grey matter getting greyer, now no more that hobbledehoy life full of happiness, curiosity, and passion to fly high. Gradually my feet rested on the ground, no more flying on cloud nine, mind engrossed in domestic needs, earnings to match expenses, insurance, bank loans, income tax, and what not! In the process, I got glasses on my nose bridge, tight lips, measured smiles, well-ironed spotless dresses, and diplomatic words. And one more thing, over the years my hairline receded, forehead became wider, so wide that it spread up to my occiput. Now no more fear of deadly pneumonia as rainwater would not stay a second on my shiny egghead.

"Darling, you are bald!" said Monica as she moved her soft palms on my head.

"Bald! What are you saying, even now I have enough hair on my head, try counting – you shall never finish counting – so much hair I have", said I.

"You must realise, dear, that you have become an egg-head! Never mind, you look more mature, intelligent, wise, and besides, more patients will come to you now as you look like a dignified doctor now", she said softly to assuage my hurt feelings.

But her talks could not pacify me. I must not look bald. Let me grow some plantations on my dry, desert-like head. So came many creams, lotions, mineral supplements, vitamins, ayurvedic oils, and what not. But the infertile land that it was, it did not grow even an extra strand of hair, forget about a dense forest.

So now what to do? Well, let me have a WIG! But I must not tell Monica about it, let it be a surprise.

Soon arrived a WIG, lovely dark hair woven on a net and I remained glued to the mirror for hours, analyzing the looks that I would achieve with different designs. After searching and analyzing many, I selected one similar to a Bollywood superstar's and soon I had a crowning glory - A WIG!

As Monica entered my room, she let out a big scream as if she saw a ghost. "Oh you, with a WIG! Oh no! You looked so nice without it".

"See now I am no more an egghead. And see how smart I look", I said.

Despite all her protests and arguments, I insisted on wearing the new crown, the WIG.

As I embraced her to comfort her, she spoke out her heart. "Please remove this wig. I feel so strange…as if not you, but some stranger is embracing me…such an awkward feeling".

Stranger, embracing my Monica? Never even in my dreams!

Next moment, I threw my WIG into the dustbin.

22.10.2017

# Most Serene Place in the Universe

I have an eagerness to explore places. With my urge to discover the most tranquil place, I have globe-trotted to the great Himalayas, the Swiss Alps, Table Mountain of Cape Town, Mt. Fuji in Japan, various sea beaches, and lonely islands. Ultimately realization dawned on me that the most serene place exists in a corner of my own home - the loo!

The moment I sit on a toilet seat, my thoughts start navigating at a lightening speed, hovering around the whole universe. Undisturbed, all the philosophies of the world strike my serene mind.

Not long ago, people used the fields to relieve themselves. It must have been a heavenly feeling to relieve in the lap of nature, listening to the music of chattering birds. Not anymore. Now you can't even contest an election if you do not have a toilet at home!

All great discoveries of the world originated from the toilet. Remember Archimedes, the ancient Greek mathematician? His eureka moment came while he was in the bath.

Gandhi, Father of the Nation, used to keep a set of pens and writing pad near his toilet. Many of his thoughts originated there. In his journey from Mohandas to Mahatma, the toilet played a significant role. Everyone knows about his brouhaha with Kasturba on the issue of toilet.

All great strategies of the government revolve around toilet. For example, the *Swachha Bharat* campaign. The government has realised, although late, that all problems originate from a dirty toilet. If the toilet is clean, the mind is clean. If mind is clean, character and attitude get cleaner and soon that cleanliness spreads around. Take for example, Japan. You will not find even a little trash anywhere in Japan. The crime rate in Japan is abysmally low. Japanese hospitality is best in the world. It is all because of their toilets. Japanese toilets are the best in the world.

What is so special about Japanese toilets? Well, as you sit on the seat, it welcomes you with warmth; the seat is automatically adjusted to a comfortable temperature. Once you finish, just press a button and a nozzle sprays a jet of warm water, directed at the proper spot and you are clean! Your hands are free for more important tasks.

The toilet is the 'Do Not Disturb' zone. If an employee is not in his seat, the explanation is, "*Babu* has gone to the toilet". No more questions are asked.

During our school's annual examinations, if the questions were tough, students would visit the loo more often. It was thought to be a natural urge after seeing difficult questions. Once, as too many students made a beeline to the loo, the invigilator got suspicious and he visited there. Not surprisingly, loads of chits for cheating were found inside the toilet!

While sitting in the toilet you can easily forget time. Seconds turn into minutes, minutes to hours. As I write this article while sitting on the toilet seat, Monica, my sweet wife screamed, "Darling, should I serve your lunch and dinner inside as well?"

20.4.2018

# A Tale of Two Friends

Circumstances change our attitude.

What may appear obviously wrong today may seem appropriate tomorrow. The same situation or event may appear proper or may appear totally bizarre depending on which side of the fence we are sitting.

Ramu and Raman are two close friends who studied together in a primary school in a village. Ramu was the son of a farmer who continued his studies to become an agricultural graduate and devoted his life to the village only. Raman, son of a businessman, went on to become an engineer, did MBA, and settled in Mumbai. He is a top executive now.

So far so good, the stories differ from now on.

Ramu remained a middle-class person, earning just enough for his family's livelihood. He has a small farm and is happy with it. He walks a lot in his farm, grows plenty of vegetables. The people in the village know him closely and come to him often for any reason. He has many friends to talk to, and celebrate various festivals with in joy and gusto.

Raman, on the other hand, is a top executive, earns a lot, strives hard for more and more, has lots of responsibilities, has put money on shares, never gets time to walk but tends to travel by Mercedes to save time on travel and also for social reasons. He attends night parties. He has professional colleagues but no friends. He has a costly cell phone for company. Drinks and smokes are his compulsions, if not a choice. He is irritable, gets body aches, headaches, and is constantly under tension.

After a decade, Raman developed diabetes and soon hypertension followed. He had to take eight different tablets to keep his blood pressure and diabetes under control. He soon got frustrated with the chain of events. He remembered his childhood friend Ramu and decided to visit his village. Both met after three decades.

Ramu was very glad to have his friend Raman after such a long time. He gave him a bear hug and after a lot of gossip under the banyan tree, both sat for dinner together.

Raman asked Ramu, "How much do you earn?"

Ramu replied humbly, "Just enough to keep me and my family going. Few thousands, but it's enough for us".

Raman laughed at him, "Only thousands! I pay that much in tax every quarter. Well what do you drive?"

Ramu replied, "I have a bullock cart and also a bicycle, but I prefer to walk".

Raman gave him a sarcastic look, "I always travel by Mercedes. You know it costs 22 lakhs. And you know Ramu, I have a flat on 13<sup>th</sup> floor from where I can see the Arabian sea all around. That flat cost two crores". Raman looked around with pride.

"*Bhai saheb*, should I give you some more rice?" asked Ramu's wife.

"Oh no, my blood sugar will shoot up".

"Then would you like to have *jhunka bhakar, bhai saheb?* And have some *baingan bharta*. It tastes delicious if you mix it with *nimbu-achar* (lemon pickle)".

"What are you offering me, *bhabhi?* My blood pressure will go up and already I am on 5 different drugs to control it. And pickle! My doctor will go mad if he comes to know about *nimbu achar*. I am on antacids round the clock, you know", said Raman.

After the dinner, Ramu offered him *ras malai*. Again, the *Laxman rekha* of diabetes came in the way.

While departing, Raman invited Ramu and his family to Mumbai. "Why don't you come and settle in Mumbai, Ramu? I shall help you in starting a business there. There is lot of money in Mumbai, you know".

"Yah, there is, but you get diabetes, hypertension, and acidity all for free with that money. What is the use of such money which prevents one from enjoying *jhunka bhakar, nimbu achar, baigan bharta,* and *ras malai?*" said *bhabhi* innocently.

Raman thought how foolish these villagers are, while Ramu felt lucky that he did not settle in Mumbai.

31.12.2017

# Mir Jafars Are Here Again!

"**P**ower does not corrupt men; fools, however, if they get into a position of power, corrupt power" - George Bernard Shaw

History repeats itself. The political scenario that exists in India today demonstrates this aptly.

These events remind us of the Battle of Plassey that took place on 23rd June 1757, in Bengal, on the banks of Bhagirathi River, about 150 kms north of Calcutta, near Murshidabad, the then capital of the Nawab of Bengal, Siraj ud Daulah. Pôlash is an extravagant red flowering tree (Flame of the Forest) that gives its name to a small village near the battlefield.

The British, worried about being outnumbered and sure defeat, reached out to Siraj-ud-Daulah's army chief – Mir Jafar. The East India Company's army led by Robert Clive was vastly outnumbered, consisting of 950 Europeans and 2,100 native Indian sepoys and a small number of guns. The Nawab had an army of about 50,000 with some heavy artillery operated by about 40 French soldiers sent by the French East India Company. Out of the initial 50,000 army, finally only 5,000 troops were engaged in battle. Under the secret pact with British, Mir Jafar thus assembled his troops near the battlefield, but made no move to join the battle, causing Siraj-ud-Daulah's army to be defeated. Siraj-ud-Daulah fled, eventually to be captured and executed. As a result, the entire province of Bengal fell to the Company, with Mir Jafar being appointed as their puppet Nawab.

The Battle of Plassey is considered a turning point in Indian history leading to the final establishment of British Raj in India.

Breach of faith once again reared its ugly head in the battle of Srirangapatna in 1799 between the combined forces of the British East India Company and their allies, numbering over 50,000 soldiers, and the Kingdom of Mysore, ruled by Tipu Sultan with about 30,000 soldiers. Tipu Sultan's prime minister, Mir Saadiq, stabbed his own Sultan in the back to help the British forces. He pulled out the Mysore army for paying wages amid the battle, thus allowing the British forces to break down the boundary wall with almost no defence. Another ploy to help the British was the spilling of water in the basements where the Sultan's army stored its gunpowder. This made the gunpowder useless. After the Company troops had taken the city, the Sultan's body was found among the dead, shot in the head, and stripped of his jewels. These jewels are displayed with pride in the Tower of London along with which is the decorated Peacock Throne of Shah-e-Jahan.

Both the traitors, Mir Jafer and Mir Saadiq were dumped unceremoniously by the very people for whom they had betrayed their king and kingdom.

These two key events changed the history of India.

Our honourable elected representatives do not find it below their dignity to trade honesty with ministerial berths or pink notes and switch sides or change their caps.

Can we trust these honourable elected representatives, who could not remain true to their own organisation with the destiny of India?

"Democracy substitutes election by the incompetent many for appointment by the corrupt few" - George Bernard Shaw.


20.10.1999


Background – Toppling of elected government by the members of legislative assemblies who switched sides.

# What Is Your Religion, Buddy?

As she became critically ill due to acute kidney failure, her daughter passionately prayed to the Goddess Durga. With time, she recovered and went back to her hometown. Her daughter Zulekha, 22, is a devout Muslim girl who reads *Namaz* five times a day but also believes in Hindu deities. Every *Ramnavami* and *Navaratri*, she fasts for full nine days.

In last couple of months, social atmosphere has developed a shade of religious intolerance, which is dangerous and not in-tune with Hinduism - a way of life for citizens of India.

In all Hindu festivals, flowers are important ingredients for worship. If you wish to purchase fresh flowers, you must visit *Sitabuldi* flower market situated next to *Laxmi Talkies*. Every day especially on *Diwali*, *Dusshera*, *Kojagiri*, and other Hindu festivals, business worth lakhs of rupees are done in this market. Now as you purchase flowers you also need *Durva*, curd, and honey. These are also available in plenty here. And then come the things you need for rituals, like *Kumkum*, camphor, honey, wet and dry coconut, *dhoop*, cotton wick, sandalwood, turmeric, and dry wood for performing

*Yagna*. As you search for these items, you will be directed to one shop, which keeps all these ingredients, the shop of Syed Bhai. Do not be surprised, this Muslim gentleman knows the details of all materials needed for Hindu rituals and has been selling them since last 60 years.

Salma and Sahida are two staff nurses in my hospital who celebrate all festivals with us and draw *rangoli* in front of our Hindu deity with full devotion. Both also participate in *aarti*. They are not any less Muslim.

In 1990, Zulfiquar Ali, an engineering student from Chandrapur, underwent kidney transplant surgery at Mure Memorial Hospital. Madhuri and Dipak Pandhre, a devout Brahmin couple, out of love supplied his meals.

Indian Hindu heart still beats in the chest of a Muslim Pakistani national following heart transplantation done at Chennai in the year 2015.

Recently, two newborn infants got exchanged in a hospital at birth. After two years, on suspicion, a DNA test done revealed that the boy born to Hindu parents was given to a Muslim couple and vice-versa. However, both mothers decided to keep the exchanged kids, fully aware that they were born in families of different faiths.

God has created us as one but we have divided ourselves based on religion, language, and geography. Death, the absolute truth, does not differentiate between cast, creed, sex, religion, or affluence. When we bleed, blood does not show our religion. Hindu blood can be safely given to Muslims.

Ibrahim was only 14 when I called him in the middle of the night to rush to Nagpur to get kidney transplant done as a matching kidney was available. A six year old girl had met with vehicular accident and was declared brain dead. Her parents, keeping aside emotions in a corner, decided to donate her organs to needy patients. Ibrahim was youngest in the list suffering from kidney failure. Both the kidneys of the donor were transplanted into Ibrahim. He got a new lease on life. There was no rejection. Here is a Muslim boy being transplanted with two kidneys of a Hindu girl and surviving. Nature did not differentiate between Muslim and Hindu, then why do we?

Lamentably, when we common citizens want to forget these religious, caste, and creed demarcations, our politicians jump in to remind us that we are different!

Today, after 70 years of Independence, we are still identified as per our faith. An innocent child applying for admission in nursery must declare religion.

On this 26th January and onwards let us just remain Indian and nothing else!

15.10.2017

# Dawn of Alzheimer's

It was an intense moment. Kidney transplant surgery was in full swing. A lady was donating kidney to her husband. Our transplant team at Orange City Hospital was working with full concentration. There was a stony silence in the operation theatre with an occasional hushed voice of the operating surgeon, beeping of the cardiac monitor, and whirring of the ventilator.

Kidney transplantation is a surgery with difference; here a healthy person donates one kidney for saving the life of a patient suffering from kidney failure. The kidney is removed, cooled to its core, and then implanted into the patient. In this case, my patient, who was on thrice-a-week dialysis, received kidney from his brave wife. She decided to give her kidney out of love and affection for her husband to save his life.

The blood vessels were connected and soon the transplanted kidney became pink, and in a few moments, it started pouring urine, the most anxiously awaited moment for all surgeons, anesthesiologists, nurses, and most importantly for me, the nephrologist.

The surgery was successful. Donor was shifted to the room; final stitches were being put on the recipient.

67

Now I felt it necessary to attend to my other patients admitted in wards. I went to the changing room, changed with haste, and went out of the OT complex.

As I walked towards the ward, I felt my trouser was a bit too loose; it frequently slipped down. I put my hand in the pocket. There was a car key, which I thought I had given to the security guard for parking the car as I usually do. Oh, possibly I forgot to give the key to the guard that day!

While I examined patients, my trouser frequently slipped down and every time I pulled it up. It went on and on for some time till my cell phone rang, "Shiv, by any chance did you wear my trousers by mistake?" It was a frantic call from the operation theatre by my surgeon friend Dhananjay.

Now everything dawned on me. The matter became crystal clear. In a hurry, I wore the trousers of Dhananjay, our transplant surgeon. His pants were a bit loose for me and slipped down often. Oh my God, what did I do? How could I be so foolish, especially when even the colour of the pants were so different than mine?!

I ran back to the operation theatre; saw Dhananjay waiting with a surgical gown on. As I changed the dress and was back with my own trousers, the whole of the operation theatre staff and Dhananjay started laughing. Face glowing red with shame, I too joined them with a blast of laughter.

As I told this episode to Monica, my wife, she smiled back, "It's nothing new, dear. Few days back you gave a shirt for washing with few hundred rupees notes tucked in the pocket. Another day, you called our receptionist Sumanlata, while her actual name is Vasudha!"

I looked at her with bewilderment. She commented, "Problems ahead, darling. It's Alzheimer's dawning", and winked her eye with great amusement.


27.08.2017

# Awaken Hindustan!

"Viewers, it's your favourite television news channel and we have some heart-breaking news; superstar Salman, the Tiger, *dabang*, *bajrangi bhaijaan*, loving *Sallu*, has been sentenced to jail".

After intense in-depth study, honourable court has awarded a five-year sentence to the superstar of India after twenty years since his crime of killing an innocent blackbuck; fast delivery of justice indeed!

After conviction, our superstar has gone to bed without food, how sad. With tearful eyes, we are sad to say that he had to sleep on the hard floor of jail with no fan, no cooler, no air conditioner in this desert state! So cruel are the jail authorities, could not they provide a simple cushion and fan to him? Forget the poor people sleeping on mosquito-laden dirty footpaths without a grain in tummy.

Oh, what a solace, our superstar has asked for a glass of milk and bread. What a relief! Poor fella, now he shall not die of hunger. Oh, do not talk about children begging on the road.

Dear viewers, *Sallu* has slept from 8 am to 11 am again. He must be tired. Our star was so tired by not sleeping at night that he could no more avoid sleep in morning hours. Do not talk about the millions who have already started work in scorching heat with empty stomachs.

Breaking news; our star has workout in the jail for three long hours in this hot summer. See, this shows how health conscious he is! Do not ask about the labourers on the street working in harsh weather.

Breaking news again; the sisters of our star have flown in to meet their brother in jail in the afternoon. No problem if you throw away the jail manual in trash cart. Oh, it's a very emotional scene, sisters meeting brother. Shed tears, *Hindustan*! Don't you have emotions? Do not talk about the many brothers rotting in jail without trial.

It took a whole twenty years for an honourable judge to pronounce a judgement after detailed study but in two days all arguments swept aside and the accused was granted bail. See, how sensitive and kind our legal system is. What a relief!

The judiciary is same for all. It does not differentiate between rich and poor, intellectual, or illiterate, star and dust. So true! Out of 4.2 lakh prisoners in India, two-third are under trials, languishing in jail without being convicted of crime. But forget it, our heartthrob *Sallu* is out of the dungeon.

Also, forget about the poor soldiers dying of stone pelting in Kashmir, forget about the bone-chilling frontiers of the nation, forget about water scarcity, forget lack of jobs, forget environmental pollution, forget corruption in public life but be happy, dear Hindustan, Salman has been released!'

7.04.2018

*Background- In April 2018, Bollywood star Salman Khan was arrested for a crime and released within few hours of arrest by the judiciary.*

# Dance of Democracy

**H**eydays are here again!

Rambhajan Pandya is extremely glad these days. The whole society has started displaying religious inclination. People from all walks of life are thronging in the temples. There are long queues outside temples. The people who never ever visited temples are now seen praying to God with sandalwood paste smeared on their foreheads. Pandya is a priest in a village near Jamnagar, Gujarat. He hopes that this religious sentiment continues even when the elections are over.

Imran Naqvi is also very glad, last few days were very hectic; more the work more is the money. What he earned in last few days will last for the whole year. He, with his three kids, toiled for eighteen hours a day the last one month. His day started at 5 am and continued till late night. He supplied plastic chairs, caps, cutouts of leaders, masks etc., for election rallies. These rallies ranged from independent candidates to rival political parties. So, he was selling white, green, orange, and black caps.

Dhanno Patil with his family had to go to bed empty stomach very often. For the last one and a half month,

73

he did not have to worry. He moved from one rally to another. Be it Congress or BJP, Shiv Sena or the communists, he changed his cap three times a day. For attending each rally, he would get a few hundred rupees plus free snacks and lunch besides free rides. He behaved like a king for the last few days. He wished for more frequent elections.

Gatya Bewda was called Bewda because of his addiction to country-made liquor. He got his daily allowance of a few pegs free of charge last couple of weeks with a promise to vote for a party. He promised multiple parties and got his quota of liquor from all.

The rickshaw pullers, van owners, drivers, tea vendors, decorators are all happy with the boom in their demands.

The paparazzo, journalists, and editors of newspapers had a field day for weeks together; they are the most sought-after people these days. There is no dearth of news to fill in the columns of newspapers. The owners of the newspapers had luck smiling over them with various political parties showering money on advertisements to woo the voters.

So are the television channels, the expert panelists, and the news anchors; all happy as they can be seen very often in the debates of TV channels throttling full volume, keen on TRPs. Sponsored television programmes, pre-managed debates, and post-election exit polls add to their income.

The income tax sleuths are happy to observe the candidates spending money like water, which they were not supposed to have. Just the thought of raiding these hidden millionaires made their palms itch.

The doctors too are happy – loud debates and loudspeakers in rallies have caused havoc with hearing. ENT specialists are happy as many are consulting them for deafness and hoarse voice. The cardiologists are happy, as their clientage will improve after the election results are out; the defeated candidates will consult them for chest pain. So are the psychiatrists who are ready with their services for treating the nervous breakdown of the defeated candidates.

They all wish that the elections were held more frequently as people celebrate the dance of democracy.

2.05.2014

# Red Rose, This 15th August

I dreamt of my garden yesterday.

My garden is full of lovely plants. Some decorative plants, some shrubs, some vegetable plants, and few full-grown trees.

I get up everyday to the melodious music of chattering birds. I open the windows with sleepy eyes and see the huge banyan tree which invites me to come out, "See how beautiful the world is!" This huge banyan tree gives cool breeze, cool shade, houses many birds, and squirrels run around on its branches.

I have a collection of lovely roses, jasmine, marigold, hibiscus, sunflower, gulmohur, chrysanthemum, lily, dahlia, and many more.

I also have a collection of thorny cactuses, varieties of them. There is a small lily pond with white and pink lilies.

Many birds - crows, *mynahas*, doves, sparrows, pigeons, parrots; dragonflies and colourful butterflies; have made my garden their home. In the branches of my banyan tree there hangs a big honeycomb. The bees swarm around buzzing and feasting on the lovely flowers.

I feel proud of my garden and humbled by Mother Nature's wonderful creation.

I dreamt of my garden yesterday.

As I strolled around my garden enjoying the cool evening breeze and wondering about the wonders of nature, I was horrified to see a parasite plant *dodder cuscata* or *amarbel*. It had invaded my garden and had spread its tentacles all around. It would be the nemesis of my lovely garden if uncontrolled. I started thinking about how to get rid of this *amarbel* when there was a sudden commotion in my haven of peace.

I looked around. All my plants started talking. The Rose declared that he is the most powerful and beautiful of all and was the king. Chrysanthemum differed; she was the most colourful. Jasmine, not to be left behind, said she spread her fragrance far and wide. The vegetable plants claimed that they were the best as they provided food for humans.

To my horror a fight ensued among the plants.

The *amarbel* got its chance. It started embracing all the plants. The plants were so busy praising themselves and finding fault with each other that they did not notice that their end was near.

My garden soon had a deserted look and I was desperately trying to remove the *amarbel*.

I woke up with a cold sweat. Where was I? What was happening?

I ran to the window to see my garden. No, it was only a dream. The garden was intact and as lovely as it could be. As I was busy appreciating its beauty just then...ting tong...

It was the paperboy. Sipping hot tea, sitting in my verandah overlooking the garden, I scanned the headlines. My dream returned.

News of arson, suicides, dharnas, bandh, child abuse, terrorist attacks, rapes, intolerance, abduction, molestation, naxalite killings, all such horrific news filled the newspaper.

My country, my motherland, my lovely garden is in the RED ··· in danger ··· of being destroyed by my own countrymen. In our race to prove ourselves to be better than others we fail to see the destruction we are bringing onto ourselves. We are destroying our banyan tree...our nation.

On this 15th August if only I could present a symbol of love - a RED ROSE to each one...


15.08.2016

# The Memorable Dinner

Raju is my childhood friend. Forgetfulness is one of his most endearing qualities. He tends to forgive and forget. But sometimes his forgetfulness lands him in a soup. Once he took his wife to the market. On the way they got down at a petrol pump to fill up his two-wheeler. After filling up the tank he drove off to his office leaving his wife behind. He forgot that his wife had accompanied him! When he reached home late at night, he had to go to bed empty stomach. "You forgot me, your wife, at the petrol pump! I also forgot to cook food", said *Bhabhi* fuming.

Raju is a very religious person. After bathing he prays to the Sun God and offers water. Come rain or snow there is no change in his morning routine. But one fine morning I got a call from his daughter Chinki. "Uncle, come to my home urgently. Papa has sprained his ankle".

"What happened?" I asked.

"Uncle, papa went to the terrace to offer water to the Sun God and while returning in a hurry, he slipped in the stairs and sprained his ankle", said Chinki.

"So many times I've told him to offer prayers from the verandah of our flat but your friend insists on going to the terrace to offer prayers as if the prayers reach God faster from terrace", said *Bhabhi*.

"I agree with Raju. After all, the sun is nearer to the terrace than verandah", I said in a jocular tone.

Often Raju had asked me to go for dinner with him. Somehow, we could not make it. One fine day I was free and I asked him if we could go out for dinner. He agreed and off we went to one of the posh restaurants of the town. I ordered the best Nawabi dishes and why not, Raju would be paying the bills. Raju too seemed to be in a good mood and ordered his favourite Chinese dishes one after the other, doing full justice to his seven feet frame and ninety kilo weight. The waiter attending our table was more than happy to serve us. He asked whether we would like to have some dessert.

"Oh yes, bring us your best dessert".

Soon we were enjoying ice cream with hot Swiss chocolate sauce. The sumptuous dinner left us satiated and happy.

When the waiter brought our bill there was a spring in his feet. After all, here were two very satisfied customers. They would surely give him a generous tip. Expectation and suppressed joy made him look like a bloated balloon.

I took the bill and placed it in front of Raju. He gently pushed it back to me. I nudged it towards him and he shoved it to me again.

"What is this Raju? Why aren't you paying the bill?"

"Bill!" he exclaimed. "You invited me, so you pay the bill".

I reminded him that it was he who had asked me out for dinner.

"Oh yes, that was few days back. But today, you invited me. Besides, I have not brought my purse", said Raju.

I put my hand into my pocket. Oh my God! There was not a single penny.

"Raju", I said in a trembling voice. "Get ready to wash the dishes".

"Brother, can you show us the place where you wash the dishes?" I asked the confused steward.

"Why, sir?"

"We forgot to bring our purse", Raju replied, shame reflecting in his voice.

The balloon deflated. The disheartened waiter took us to the manager.

"Manager *Saheb*, thanks for your nice meal", I said.

"Thanks sir, we are here to serve you", he said politely, happy to be complimented.

"No, in fact we have come to serve you", I replied. "Kindly show us the place where you wash the dishes, as we have both forgotten our purses."

The prospect of washing dishes frightened Raju. "You can keep our watches while we go and get the money. We live close by", Raju pleaded.

I expected a good sermon from the manager but was pleasantly surprised when he said, "Do not worry sir, you may send the payment later. After all, we can judge a man from his face".

Face is the mirror of a man's heart. I had never realised that my face reflected my sincerity too. We promised to pay the bill the next morning, thanked the manager, wished him good night, and left.

Once on the streets, we walked silently with our heads hanging in shame for a good ten minutes and then as the absurdity of the situation dawned on us, we burst into laughter and hugged each other. It was past midnight and we were strolling on the streets laughing. A patrolling cop watched us suspiciously. His glare was enough to bring us back to our senses. We controlled ourselves and returned home like good citizens.

It was a dinner that I shall never forget. Memory of that sumptuous dinner with my dear friend never fails to bring a smile on my face.

22.10.1998

# The Lighter Side of Darkness

For the *aam aadmi*, i.e., the common man, load-shedding has proved to be a boon in disguise. It has instilled a sense of punctuality, endurance, and discipline among the masses, and has taught the value of money to common man.

Load-shedding has taught us the value of time. The government offices are seeing record attendance now days. The employees do not have to work as due to load-shedding the computers do not work. Once the lights are back, they can do overtime to compensate for lost hours!

Nothing can be more punctual than load shedding schedules. I often sync my watch timings with the time of load-shedding. By and large electricity departments never follow Indian standard time while applying load shedding. They possibly follow Greenwich timings, as at exact time, the lights go off.

Load-shedding may help in reducing the country's population by default. During our most crucial moments, the lights go off. When a patient is critically sick and needs to be brought to the hospital by lift, or needs to be hooked to a cardiac monitor, the lights would go off. The patients undergoing major surgeries

83

or dialysis, or infants in the premature baby unit, suffer the most.

The wives of the surgeons are very happy as they are now finding their better halves more at home than in the hospital. Their children of doctors have also started identifying their parents as the parents find more time for children due to load-shedding.

The parents are happy too. The children who had become addicted to television serials are now back to the study tables with kerosene lamps!

Earlier, due to well-lit nights, the stars in the sky were not visible but now we regularly watch the sky and wonder at the creative skills of the Creator. The moon has regained its lost glory; it blesses the world with its soothing light during load-shedding hours.

Besides human beings, the other vertebrates and invertebrates too are joyful due to load-shedding. The mosquitoes are happy, as the mosquito repellents are mostly electricity dependent. These are the days of merry making for these poor tiny creatures. After all, they also need to survive. Mosquitoes also help in controlling the country's population by inflicting human with dengue and malaria.

The mosquito-net sellers are also very happy. They had never seen such a boom in sales of mosquito nets.

The people dealing in inverters and generators are more than happy nowadays. Their sales have soared high.

Sale of petrol and diesel has also soared high, as the generators need fuel to produce power. It is but natural for the prices of these commodities to go up.

All the good and auspicious works are done during early morning hours, i.e., *bramha-muhurtum*. Similarly, all the black deeds are done in the dark hours of night. The thieves and dacoits have their heydays now, thanks to load-shedding. The petty thieves and chain snatchers are turning into full time thieves. The thieves are becoming dacoits. I wonder whether the dacoits will now think of joining politics and bring a constitutional amendment to make load-shedding compulsory!

Because of the hot climate and mosquitoes, people are not getting peaceful sleep during load-shedding. The statisticians dealing with demography are predicting that there is a likelihood of population boom for obvious reasons.

Load-shedding at times may create funny situations. In a town in South India, during a period of load-shedding, in a mass marriage ceremony, a groom garlanded a wrong bride in the darkness and a bride in turn garlanded her own friend instead of the groom. Fortunately, the wrongs were detected in the right time and then the elders of the family did the needful to rectify mistakes.

Despite so many benefits, the *aam aadmi* are the unhappy lot. These poor, stupid, so-called tolerant chaps are drained off, and virtually squeezed to the extent of intolerance due to load-shedding.

*Background – In 2010, there was extreme power shortage and frequent load-shedding in India.*

25.06.2010

# Bulls of Barcelona

It was a bone chilling experience. I was witnessing a sport in Spain which has been going on since time immemorial. It was a bullfight. With the display of the colourful band, fierce bulls rushed inside the ring arena. It found a man inside and rushed to crush him under its mighty hoofs. The man was expecting this attack so he jumped over the boundary to clear off the attacking bull. The mighty bull then started thumping its hooves on the ground. And there entered a warrior with a flag mounted on a sharp arsenal. The angry bull now attacked him but before it could pierce the man with its sharp horns, the man had pierced the sharp arsenal on the back of the ferocious bull. The crowd became ecstatic. There was appreciation all around and the man jumped the boundary wall like a hero.

The stadium was jam-packed. I reached the stadium before time lest I should be denied a ticket. My daughters accompanied me but were not allowed inside as they were below sixteen. As I stood in the queue, a squadron of horse-mounted police took up positions to ward off any kind of disruption by animal lovers who had assembled to protest the cruelty to the animals. They were people from different walks of life who assembled in front of the stadium carrying placards depicting the photographs of poor animals being injured by almighty humans. Something inside me cried aloud and I was about to return from the venue but then my curiosity won and I purchased the tickets.

It appeared to me right from the beginning that the bulls were intoxicated possibly with opium or alcoholic drinks. Their ability to judge and then attack was missing. After the sharpened arsenal pierced the bull, there entered warriors, *'picadores'*, mounted on horsebacks and armed with a sort of lance. The horses were huge, muscular, and tall; covered with protective overalls. Their eyes too were covered with cloth to prevent them from seeing the attacking bull. The frightful bull attacked the horses. The warrior sitting atop the horse attacked the bull with a sharp arrow and pierced its chest. A gush of blood came out of the wounded chest. The bull lost a lot of blood following this attack. It had become weak and confused. It was unable to understand why he should be a target of such inhumane attacks by human beings.

And then the real hero, the *'torero'*, descended on the scene. He walked up to the centre of the arena, waived his hand carrying a sword called *muleta* in one hand, and a red rag in the other. He waived the red rag at the bull. The bull rushed at him but could only attack the cloth as the warrior had moved aside. This game continued for quite a while. The warrior would enrage the bull waiving the red cloth, the bull would attack the red cloth, but the man behind would just move aside to score off the attack. The bull would get enraged further to attack with renewed vigour. But the bleeding bull was getting weaker every moment due to continuous blood loss from the inflicted wounds. Soon it was tired, anaemic, and was unable to move quickly. The hero then attacked the bull with his sharp sword to pierce its heart. The bull fell on the ground, convulsed a little, vomited blood, and soon became motionless. There was excitement all around. The crowd started shouting with joy.

This was followed by the band's music and then the second bull was deployed for the game. The same routine followed. This bull too was intoxicated, repeatedly assaulted by well-dressed and decorated warriors. Then finally, the hero assaulted the now tired and  weak, frail bull who was at the verge of death anyway due to rapid loss of blood. To my utter dismay, there were cheers all around; viewers were ecstatic with joy as their hero triumphantly killed the animal. This show was repeated many times but I could tolerate no more. My heart was pounding as if it would come out of my throat. I was saddened by the fate of the poor hapless animal. I came out halfway through this terrible show of inhumanity and pseudo-triumph.

18.06.2012

# My Three Heroes

Ahero is a person admired for courage, outstanding achievements, or noble qualities. My three heroes are all iconic due to these qualities.

While travelling in a car, the wind screen got smashed by a stone, and as luck would have it, a tiny glass fragment flew and hit the young boy's right eye and made him completely blind. The boy thanked Allah for saving his other eye and continued with his passion of cricket to become the youngest captain of Indian cricket team and of the world at that time. He led the team from the front, he was Tiger Pataudi. He is my hero because he did not allow his misery to overtake his passion and continued to keep the Indian flag flying high.

If in the height of career, a person is struck with cancer, it is sufficient to devastate him physically and mentally. But the person I am talking about did not bend, did not bow down to lung cancer, but after struggling for a few years, not only defeated it but also sprang back and blasted the balls with full might beyond boundaries for sixes and fours. He is Yuvraj Singh, the man with a mission and passion.

Bubbling with energy, even after a gap of two years due to cancer chemotherapy, he went on knocking the doors of selectors with his determined performance in domestic cricket to get into the national team again. He not only batted well but was also the highest wicket-taker for India in World Twenty20 series in 2012. In 2015 IPL tournament, he was bought by Delhi Dare devils for a mammoth Rs 16 Crores. I salute his courage and resolve.

She is one of the finest orators. Once she starts her debate in parliament, people are dumbfounded. She has never hit anyone below the belt and has been a favourite of even her opposition. She was struck with kidney failure due to diabetes. I see so many people who find their life crumbling down once they are declared to have failed kidneys but she had the guts to stand up against it, get a kidney transplant, and jump back into politics. She is our beloved Minister of Foreign Affairs, Sushma Swaraj; the minister with sympathy and empathy, full of humanitarian qualities, who is ever ready to help any person in distress anywhere in the world irrespective of cast, creed, religion, gender, or nationality. Recently a Pakistani lady suffering with heart ailment commented that she wished Sushma were the Prime Minister of Pakistan instead!

It is very easy to blame destiny and shrink into a corner doing nothing, blaming everything on circumstances and getting lost in the tide of time. Only those who keep their desire burning, and allow its flame to light their path, achieve glory.

1.09.2017

*Mohammad Mansoor Ali Khan Siddiqui, Mansur Ali Khan, or M.A.K. Pataudi (5 January 1941 – 22 September 2011), nicknamed Tiger Pataudi, was an Indian cricketer and former Indian Captain. He was adjudged as best fielder. He had lost his right eye in an accident.*

** Yuvraj Singh, Indian Cricketer, who had cancer of the lungs, came back to play after getting cured.*

*** Sushma Swaraj, Ex-Foreign Minister of India, who had kidney failure and had kidney transplant. She joined back after treatment and was known for her humanitarian approach to problems faced by Indians.*

# National Labour Pain

S he was pregnant.

The whole family was full of joy as well as anxiety. The impending arrival of a newborn was a matter of joy while everyone in the family was nervous about uncertainties.

The doctor had predicted that it's going to be a difficult labour. The foetus is lying horizontal in the womb and may cause obstructed labour, inducing intense pain. Even in the process of delivery, the foetus may not survive. This may even harm the mother.

After listening to the family doctor, there was an intense discussion among the family members.Some said, "Why don't you abort? Let the foetus die, avoid pain, and save the life of the mother". After lot of ifs and buts and heated arguments, the family thought of taking another opinion.

So, the family called for an expert. The experienced doctor arrived, a bit old in his early sixties, slightly bald, with white hair and beard, sharp eyes, a roaring voice, and short temper who does not care a bit about opinions but has a  face bright with wrinkles of wisdom.

"Humm…" said the thoughtful doctor.

93

"Kho…kho…what hum, doctor? The mother will not survive, that's what you mean doc, is it not?" said the pessimist brother-in-law suffering from chronic cough.

"Humm means the foetus will not survive… I am sure", said another pessimist sister-in-law who always remained angry without a reason.

"Humm…oh doc, you mean everything will be okay, right?" said the optimist father.

The wise and experienced doctor looked around, asked everyone to go out, and conducted tests in privacy behind closed doors. He examined the would-be mother, placing his hand tenderly over the palms of the expectant lady. Then he opened the doors and came out of the room.

All family members surrounded the old physician.

"Yes doc, what do you think?" asked the mother in law.

The doctor prescribed some medicines and with determination declared, "She will need forceps delivery. It will hurt but she will deliver a healthy baby".

"No, no, how can she…kho…kho…after all, she has obstructed labour", said brother-in-law coughing due to anxiety and tension. Somehow, he was hell bent on proving himself right. The sister-in-law agreed with him.

The elderly doctor looked at him with sharp eyes without uttering a word.

After a few tense hours, the lady delivered a healthy child.

Oh, what a relief, everyone erupted with joy, excepting two, the coughing brother-in-law and the always-angry sister-in-law.

After delivery, labour pains were forgotten. Everyone thanked the old experienced physician for his skill and art of conducting such a difficult delivery.

I mused...it is the state of affairs in our Mother India. The corruption had engulfed her to such an extent that it needed an expert wise man to purge it off. One of the ways was demonetization.

The process is like a painful labour. Many poor people were inconvenienced but once these teething problems are overcome, the fruit of this whole process of demonetization will be immense. It will help the economy by crushing the parallel shadow economy. Banks will be rich enough to lend money to the poor. The hoarders and black marketers will perish. There will be more money with the government for developing infrastructure like roads, canals, railways, metro, smokeless power plants. There will be equal opportunities for all children to study the stream of their choice, equal opportunity for employment without bribe. There will be equal justice for all. No one shall escape the law of the land just because he is rich.

This purging has also broken the backbone of terrorists; be it naxalites or so called jehadis of Kashmir. We hope that this step will usher in a new ray of hope for the country.

Labour is always painful, but once delivered, it's joy all around.

*Background- *On 8 November 2016, the Government of India announced the demonetization of all Rs 500 and Rs 1,000 banknotes of the Mahatma Gandhi Series. People seeking to exchange their banknotes had to stand in lengthy queues and faced hardships.*

26.12.2016

# No Lamps This Diwali

Diwali, the festival of lights. Every year we light the lamps and welcome goddess Laxmi and celebrate the festivities with fanfare. But this year my heart has bled so much that my hands are too tremulous to light the lamps.

*Nirbhaya* was a lovely girl, full of enthusiasm, studying in a college in Delhi, far from her village. She had thought of becoming a medical professional, earn money, make a name, and support her family. But her life was sucked out by devils in a running bus who thrashed her, outraged her, and took away her honour in a most heinous manner and threw her out of the running bus. She went on fighting, fought for her life, did not lose hope; she wanted to survive, survive for her dearest mother, but in vain. When our daughters are treated this way, tell me dear friends, with such blinded wisdom, can we offer prayers to goddess *Laxmi*? How can we light the lamps this *Deepawali*?

Gopal uncle went for *Char Dham yatra*, never to come back from *Kedarnath*. He has not returned yet. Octogenarian Sudha granny still looks at the door. At times she goes out of the house into the narrow lane and looks at the distant dusty path, whether her son could be seen. He had promised her to bring *prasad* from *Kedarnath*. I look at her malnourished frail body, barely able to walk; her only son Gopal was the apple of her eyes. He wished to take Sudha granny with him but for her age. Her diminished vision with cataract gave her hope every now and then. Every human form at a distance looked like her son. "Oh, Oh, my Gopal has come", she would cry with joy, till the approaching human form betrayed her hopes. I cannot find the courage to tell her, "Look granny, your *Gopal* shall never come back!" Tell me dear friends, with such a heavy heart, how can I light the lamps this *Deepawali*?

Aabidah has been staying in the relief camp near *Muzaffarnagar* since almost 2 months. Her husband has been mercilessly killed, sister gang raped, house burnt, property looted. Her whole world has collapsed in front of her eyes in no time. She has not uttered a word since then. She has become mute and dumb with shock. She looks blankly into the blue sky, trying to search the reason for why the fate has been so cruel to her. Her lifeless eyes without any sparkle makes my fingers numb.

How can I celebrate the festival of lights in my home when my sister Aabidah's home has plunged into eternal darkness? Tell me dear friends, how can I light the lamps this *Deepawali*?

29.11.2013

*Background - \*Nirbhaya – In 2012, a young girl was gang raped and fatally assaulted in a moving bus in New Delhi.*

*\*\*In June 2013, there was a sudden rapid melting of ice and snow on the Kedarnath Mountain, 6 km (3.7 mi) from the temple, which flooded the Charbari lake (upstream) and then Kedarnath. The temple was flooded with water, resulting in several deaths due to drowning and panic-driven stampede. Many pilgrims who went for Char Dham yatra died.*

*\*\*\* Muzaffarnagar - Hindu-Muslim riots took place in August 2013, which resulted in loss of many lives.*

# Smiling Left-hander

She had a pretty face adorned with an enigmatic smile. She was a black beauty and had I been a poet, I would have likened her to a black pearl, such was her radiance. Her soft lilting voice, her dark wavy hair dancing on her forehead, and graceful walk held our attention.

We met her during our short trip to Kerala. As we drove from Cochin to Periyar, we wished to quench our thirst with fruit juice. From a distance we could see a shop where fresh pineapple juice was being sold. As we stopped for a drink, the black beauty rushed towards our car. There was a spring in her steps and a welcome smile on her face. She was wearing a simple handloom sari and had a white *dupatta* thrown casually over her right shoulder. She ushered us to her single room mud house and made us sit comfortably on a bench made of bamboo and wood. She quickly arranged for a bamboo tripod which she lifted with her left hand and arranged in front of us in as decorative manner as was possible in her hut. Behind the hut was a small farm full of pineapple plants. They were selling freshly picked pineapple juice.

The black beauty ran to the farm with a sickle, plucked a pineapple with her left hand, then dissected it into small pieces with a fine knife   and then she put the pieces into a juicer. She moved the gear of the juicer with her left hand   and the fresh juice started pouring into a container.

Then she poured the juice into big glasses and brought the tray to our table with her left hand, keeping it on the bamboo tripod, and served us smilingly. As we asked her about the farm, she answered in broken Hindi mixed generously with Malayali. Though we could not understand everything she was saying, we could understand that she and her husband had been working on the farm for many years. They looked after the farm and attended to any thirsty travellers who stopped by to have a drink. They stayed in a tiny hut on the farm itself. Every evening the landlord came and collected the day's earning.

I took the glass and moved around in the farm behind the hut, and after I had finished the drink, I handed over the glass to the black beauty, which she took with her left hand. I thanked her for the nice juice and for her hospitality, paid the bill and continued our journey.

As we drove ahead, my daughter asked me, "Papa, did you notice something strange about that lady?"

I thought and answered, "Oh yes, she was working with her left hand only".

"That was because she had no right hand. She had lost her right hand in an accident long back", replied my wife. I was astonished. I looked back towards the hut. There stood the black beauty waving at us with her left hand and a beautiful heavenly smile on her serene face.

"God has gifted us with so much but we understand the importance of such divinely gifts only when we lose them. See this young lady who has lost her hand but look how happy she is. Even in this dire poverty where she and her family are practically living hand-to-mouth, she can smile, forgetting that she has lost her right hand. Look at the radiance on her face. She is helping her family from dawn to dusk. She is content. She has no grudges", said my wife.

We were all dumbfounded. We all live but only a few live fully.


20.10.2015

# King for a Few Moments

By default, I was a king for a few moments.

It was a flight from Nagpur to Mumbai by our 'international' domestic carrier. As I entered the aircraft, I handed over the boarding pass to the airhostess. Interestingly, and to my utter surprise, after seeing the boarding pass, she bowed down and respectfully ushered me to a seat. She asked me with a divine smile on her face, "How do you do, Sir?" She was an edifice of humility.

Soon followed another hostess. She presented me with an ice-cold towel to clean my face with. After a grueling day at Nagpur, it was refreshing indeed. As I finished, another beauty followed with a tray, "What would you like to have, sir, fresh lemon juice or water melon juice?" I obliged her and asked for watermelon juice.

By now I grew suspicious. Am I dreaming? Am I in a real world or in a wonderland? Or did I rub a magical lantern like Aladdin?

I have flown to Mumbai on innumerable occasions but never did I have such a grand welcome. I looked around. The seats were broad, spacious, and very comfortable. There was a separate tray holder with each seat along with extra leg space. The seat cushion was more than comfortable. Oh, at last our national carrier has changed its style of functioning - could be due to tough competition from other airlines. Competitions are beneficial to passengers - so I thought.

As I was getting adjusted to the VIP treatment, I was further pampered by another airhostess. "Sir, which magazine would you like to read?" said she in a melodious voice. She had brought 15 chronicles to choose from. Wow, great! The airline has changed for good, I thought.

Now time was ripe for the aircraft to leave Nagpur. An officer from the ground staff came to check the number of passengers in the aircraft. Soon he was dialing to the airport check-in counter, "Sir, you said two executive class passengers, I find three here". Now the things became crystal clear to me. I was offered a wrong seat. In place of usual cattle-class, I mean economy class, I was ushered in to executive class seat by mistake and hence all the pampering!

Soon I was back to my original seat in poor cattle-class with congested seats, neglected. 'Care-you-not' airhostesses, torn outdated news papers in the cabin, passengers sitting next to me with dry parched throat, none of the airhostesses bothering to bring water even after asking, forget about fruit juices, icecold towels and up to date chronicles.

I sighed a sense of relief when passengers of both the classes reached the same destination i.e., *'aamchi* Mumbai.'

15.07.2017

# Curse of Gandhari

Thousand years ago…

In the aftermath of *Mahabharata* war, Gandhari was bitter with the death of her hundred sons. She realised that like her even Draupadi had lost all her sons. All this for some piece of land! Could it not have been averted? She asked Krishna, "Krishna, look around you; so much death and devastation. All this happened for what? It was so futile. They died for some absurd reason and their deaths defy any logic! You could have prevented this war if you wished so, but you did not, oh Krishna! You are responsible for this calamity!"

The blindfolded queen spoke with contempt, "You could have averted this war, Krishna! You should have stopped all this from happening. You should have stopped the pointless and meaningless death of so many people. Why didn't you?"

Then she screamed a curse, "May you, Krishna, witness the death of your children and your children's children. And may you die alone in the forest, hunted down like a beast". Gandhari spoke venomously, "so listen to my words and listen them well! You and your people will kill each other and die...every last one of you..." The Pandavas gasped as Gandhari continued. "And you Krishna, thirty-six years from now, when you die, you will have no one near you! No one to talk to and you will also die unattended like my sons! These are the words of the mother whose hundred sons you killed".

The mighty time passed by...

Few thousand years later, in the land of Kuru again, there was a fight. The fight for the throne of the biggest state of India, Uttar Pradesh. This time for legislative assembly.

Again, the Yadav clan was on one side ready to fight. They must win this election. All family members; elders, youngers, sons, brothers, daughter-in-laws; almost twenty-five of the family members jumped into the election battlefield. By hook or crook, win was a must.

But...

The curse of Gandhari followed. Thousands of years prior, she had said, "You and your people will kill each other and die...every last one of you...". Only definitions changed. Now death meant getting extinguished politically.

We saw a bitter power struggle within *Samajwadi* Party established by the eldest clan member of Yadavas, Mulayam Singh Yadav. He and his brother Shivpal removed his son Akhilesh from the party and again reinstated. In turn Akhilesh replaced his father as the president of the party, uncle Shivpal was shown the door and again brought in, mother-in-law abused step son, daughter-in-laws jumped into poll fray. Each one caught each other's throat; there was a bitter fight, result was as expected. Yadav clan lost the election battle. They were wiped out of the political arena, albeit temporarily.

The elder Yadav who had built up the kingdom (Party) bit by bit has no one to talk to...politically isolated, unattended, and extinguished.

The curse of Gandhari passed on from generations to generation. Gandhari 's curse came true to devastating efficacy.

16.12.2017

*Background- In the assembly elections of Uttar Pradesh held in the year 2017, Samajwadi Party had a big stake but because of internal dissensions within the family, the party lost miserably.*

# My Hostel Days

It was a warm lazy winter Sunday. No exams on head. We gossiped throughout the morning, and had a good sumptuous lunch of the month, the so-called feast.

The feast was special in the sense that on that day a sweet item from the menu would be served unlimited. Ramlakhan bhau, the mess contractor, would try to offer less and our friends would see to it that they do full justice to the money they had paid as mess fees (in Hindi it's called 'paisa wasool').

To the utter dismay of Ramlakhan bhau, there used to be a competition to test who could gulp maximum *gulab-jamuns*. In the process almost every one of hostel boys would gulp 20 or more *gulab-jamuns*. Someone had set a record of 60 *gulab-jamuns* at one go after finishing his routine meals!

There was only one copy of a Hindi newspaper in the mess, and we would lick every sentence of it. In the meantime, my one energy-packed colleague nicknamed AG, daring man that he was, climbed up the hostel building to terrace and instead of coming down the stairs, jumped every floor over the window shades till he reached down. We looked with drooping jaws and our hearts in our mouths.

A day prior, our whole herd of second year boys were driven out in the middle of the icy cold night by 'bosses' of senior class who got bored of studying and were searching for an excuse to freshen up their tired brain. As if the chilly weather was not cold enough, we all were made to shed our clothing and sit in front of the hostel entrance with our naked buttocks touching the sharp cold stone pebbles. To make the matter worse and hence more memorable, chilly ice-cold water was poured on our head from the top of the building. But bosses were not at all heartless, they felt pity on us and to make us warm, we, in our birthday dresses, were asked to run around the hostel at 3 am midnight. So much of their kindness!

Naturally with such grueling at night, circus by AG in the morning, and a belly full of delicious gulab-jamun in the afternoon, we were a bit sombre and eyes were drooping with strong urge to sleep. As we were trying to catch up with a bit of sleep, we were widely awakened by a mysterious sound on the ground floor of the hostel. We rushed down only to find some of our peers running from one end of the corridor to the other making a sound that resembled a bleating goat...may...mae...me...mey...umm...ummmm....mey ...may...me...meey.

What happened? How come mass hysteria affected so many boys!

I saw my friends coming out of a room with wide smiles and an immense sense of heavenly satisfaction writ on their faces. It so happened that we had a big playground in front of hostel number five. Often domestic animals used to graze around in that ground. One of our peers on ground floor caught hold of a goat, slaughtered it in the room, cooked it, and gave a lavish party to his close friends. After the party, they started running around in the veranda bleating like a goat as if the goat in their stomach was bleating through their mouth!

After the sun had set, the darkness of the winter evening was gradually embracing the horizon. An old man profusely sweating in the chilly evening was frantically searching for his goat, which was lost somewhere near the hostel.

My heart ached to hear the loud laughter emanating from one of the rooms.

17.11.2017

# Corrosion to the Core

There was a big banyan tree by the side of a lake in my village. It gave shade and a cool breeze. It had thick aerial roots, which descended from its branches and had spread over a huge area. Children used these aerial roots as swings. It was house to many birds, squirrels, and monkeys. It was pleasant to listen to their melodious chattering.

We had a Shiva temple beneath it. Locals would worship, offer flowers, water, and sweets. Daily evening, elders of the village would sit beneath this tree and gossip. For centuries this banyan tree stood as a trademark of our village.

The lake was the lifeline of our village. People would fetch water for drinking and for watering the plants. Fishermen would catch fish and sell there. Fresh fish was always available. The villagers would bathe their cattle in one corner of the lake. There was greenery everywhere and cattle were seen grazing happily around.

In the evening a cool breeze would embrace us while we strolled around the lake.

At that time I used to see flock of birds flying with various formations, twisting, and turning in unison. At night, I used to gaze at the stars. My father would point at a bright star in the sky, "Look, these are a conglomeration of seven stars called *Saptarshi* and if you draw a straight line from there, you can see the bright star called *Dhruva tara*".

I left my village for higher studies. After few decades I visited my village again. I found the lake had been replaced by a concrete jungle. The banyan tree had been chopped off. There was no shade, no chattering birds, no squirrels, or monkeys. The fields and grasslands had disappeared. I could not see any crow or sparrow. The evening gatherings of elders had disappeared.

There was no shade, my cool village had become warm and there was a long queue for water by the side of a municipal tap with people fighting for every single drop.

The greed of people had destroyed the village. Thoughtless constructions had destroyed the natural resources causing havoc.

The children who used to be seen enjoying swings under the shade of the banyan tree are now busy in coaching classes shaping their future or are engrossed in newfound games on mobiles.

There was no greenery or cattle. Evening was silent. Gone were those chirping birds and murmurs.

The society is changing rapidly. But this change must be thoughtful. I had been to Japan recently. Japan has severe limitation of space due to its geography and there are problems related to dense population. But I have not seen dirt, garbage, or a mad thoughtless concrete jungle there.

Let there be progress but we must not corrode the core or else society will collapse due to its own burden.

09.08.2011

# The Atheist

Dhananjay, my friend, was a pure atheist. He believed in no God. Life is a result of an accident, he used to say. Out of millions of cells, one cell accidentally meets another and there begins life. Cells multiply and grow into a tissue to give rise to a form, either plant or animal depending on the chromosomal makeup which by themselves are made up of chemicals called nucleic acids namely DNA.

"If it is so then how come you are different from me? Why you are fairer and I, wheatish? You have a sharp nose and about my nose, the less said is better...", I said. "Depending upon the codes or sequence of the nucleic acids i.e., DNA, a person can be fair or dark, dwarf or tall, thin or obese, have ears like elephants or eyes like owl, intelligent like me or dull like you", he replied. In other words, it's not God but it's the DNA which matters.

"Your forefathers were amoeba, hydra, fish, frog, and monkey. After millions of years of evolution, finally you have lost the tail and became what you are now", he joked.

Instantly I placed my hand on the back of my spine and realised that what Dhananjay had said was true. I do have a bone called tail bone!

"So Dhananjay you believe there is no God, and we are just the accidental creations of a conglomeration of some chemicals. So what will happen once we die?"

"Simple", replied my intelligent friend "Once the cells get old, they will die, meaning thereby we shall die. And if we are burnt after death then we shall form carbon, water, maybe some nitrogen, and if buried then our body chemicals will decompose into a compound that will be helpful as fertiliser to plants. That's the end of it, simple".

"Then what about emotions; love, lust, anger, pain, happiness…?"

"These are also a result of chemicals like adrenalin, nitrous oxide, dobutamin, etc." , he replied.

"So, you mean there is no existence of soul, and there is no God?" I asked.

"God is the greatest lie of the world", he said. "It is a myth created by people for their own gain. Some cunning fellows put a sense of guilt among simple people to run a business called religion. There is nothing like soul. Everything ends with the death of cells".

"Then what about sun, moon, day and night? Why do they have a fixed schedule and pattern?" I asked.

116

"It's simple mathematics and physics. They move around in orbit and are bound by a gravitational force".

Thus, he implied that whether living or non-living, everything in the world is nothing but chemical and physical property of matter which follows a mathematical rule and God does not exist.

After few days, I had to go to attend the cremation of a relative of a friend of mine. There were hundreds of people at the cremation ground. It was an atmosphere of sadness. After cremation, all the people sat around the bereaved family, said few words of praise for the departed person, and then started chanting the name of God. "Hare Rama, Hare Rama, Hare Krishna, Hare Krishna".

Among the crowd, I felt as if I heard the voice of a known person. I looked around; it was Dhananjay, the atheist, chanting the name of God with closed eyes!

17.06.2016

# The Steel Gates of Ramdaspeth

As I was taking a morning stroll in Dagdi park in Ramdaspeth, our semi-residential locality, I saw remains of four strong steel gates and a deserted guard's cabin. These reminded me of incidents behind these gates. There are too many lessons in this true story, so it is worth to dwell into little depth for some take-home messages.

About a decade prior, there were few episodes of theft in Ramdaspeth area. Few friends, who grew up together, studied and played together, were saddened to see such thefts, and were worried for the safety of the locality. They dwelt on the problem of these thefts and discussed how to prevent these. They decided that the residents of the locality should be united to solve this problem. Some more residents came together and formed an association with an aim to protect the locality from theft.

People contributed and with the kitty they started activities. Four big steel gates were constructed. By the side of these gates was the security guards' cabin. Security guards were employed for round the clock duty.

Along with the security, the association started holding social get-togethers for celebrating Ganesh festival, *Dusshera, Deepawali,* etc. The association soon became very rich. Money poured in; coffers swelled. Money begets money, it also begets power, and power begets politics. Wherever there is money, politics, and power, there is strife. Soon there formed power centres and soon a very calm, quiet, resilient, tolerant society, turned into a seat of dirty politics. The unity crumbled and peace broke into pieces.

Now, the deserted guard cabins and abandoned costly steel gates are shedding silent tears.

Decade old friends now avoid each other, if someone heads south, other will move north. Such is their repulsion, all for the sake of unity to begin with!


24.07.2017

# History Repeats Itself

There were innumerable kings in the world but history remembers only three kings who are regarded as great; Ashok, Alexander, and Akbar (Ashok the great, Alexander the great, and Akbar the great). They are regarded as great because not only were they very powerful and masters in tactical maneuvers, but because of their humane quality of forgiving even the staunchest enemies.

"Treat me as a king would treat another king", said Porus when captured by Alexander in the battle of Hydaspes on the banks of Jhelum river fought in 326 BC. Benevolent Alexander returned the land and allowed Porus to continue ruling his kingdom as his subordinate.

Vengeful Ashok, as a warrior, won a huge stretch of Indian subcontinent from present day Afghanistan in east to Bangladesh on west before embracing Buddhism (about 250 BC). India prospered and flourished under this great emperor.

Akbar the great, though illiterate, was able to rule this large Indian subcontinent as he treated his subjects well, made friends with his enemies, and people of other religions like King Sawai Mansingh of Jaipur (16th Century).

On the other hand, we also had treacherous kings like Muhammad Ghori who captured Prithviraj Chauhan after being defeated repeatedly and every time forgiven (11th Century).

When captured, Prithviraj was brought to Ghori. He looked straight into the eyes of Ghori which infuriated the latter and he mercilessly scooped out the eyes of Prithviraj, making him blind.

History tells us that the blind Prithviraj killed Ghori with an arrow while demonstrating 'shabd bhedi baan vidya' (firing an arrow on the target just by listening to sound). Today, tombs of Ghajni and Prithviraj lie adjacent to each other in Afghanistan.

Those who do not remember the past are condemned to repeat it. India has tried to make friends with neighbouring countries on innumerable occasions. Remember Vajpayee's bus ride to Lahore to shake hands with Sharif and the gift of Kargil war in return, and later with Musharraf in Agra only to be stabbed on the back later by violence in Kashmir. Modi went to shake hands with Sharif to Lahore but was gifted with the Pathankot attack.

We must take our steps keeping in mind past deeds and not get moved by emotions, as history tends to repeat itself.

13.11.2019

# As a PM in Dreams

The day has been full of activity; so many events, so many actions, orations, and gatherings. The country is going through turmoil. While watching the television, I went into a trance and then…

In front, appeared the Minister of Home Affairs, "Sir", he said, "we are in great trouble, sir".

"What happened?" I asked.

"There are no rooms available, sir", informed the anxious home minister.

"Which rooms are you talking about, mister home minister?" I asked.

"Rooms in the prison, sir. Already thousands are lodged inside and court has sentenced few hundreds more, sir. As of today, many cases are in process, sir".

The home minister was in panic. "And the way the honourable courts are delivering the judgements, sir, soon we will have no place in the prison", said the home minister in a trembling voice.

"Are there so many criminals this time of the year?" I was astonished.

"No and yes, sir. Not usual criminals, they are all our respected, honourable, elected politicians who committed various scams, sir. Coal gate, 2G, 3G, Commonwealth scam, Adarsh scam, Fodder scam, MBBS admission scandal, defense purchases scandal, and many more that are under the carpet. Then there are the politicians jailed for instigating riots, sir", replied the home minister.

"Few of the religious gurus, the God-men, with their followers are also lodged in the jail, sir, for irreligious devilish activities", the minister reminded me.

I too was worried. With so many scams, so many politicians of different hues and shades, so many religious swamis and gurus, I am sure we shall need to create more prisons. The home minister continued further, increasing my worry.

"Now there is one more problem. Five hard core militants have escaped from the prison, sir."

"Very good", I replied. "Now we can have these five rooms for politicians"."But once we catch those militants, where will we lodge them, sir?"

"Easy, we will keep them in the homes of those police officers whose negligence resulted in their escape", I replied.

"There is one more problem, sir", there was no end to his worries.

"Now what?" I asked.

"These political prisoners are asking for separate prison. One for secular politicians and other for communal ones. How can we have such different prisons, sir?"

the confused home minister asked me.

"I am also getting enquiry from various political parties about vacancy of good prison rooms. They want to book rooms for their leaders in advance just in case they need these in future", I revealed the secret.

"Sir, in next session of parliament, these political parties are going to bring prison reform bill", the home minister continued.

"As per their wish and connections, we need to provide them with good air-conditioned rooms, good food, personal attendants, pan, tobacco, television, mosquito nets, mobile, and a mike, sir", said the minister.

"Why mike?" It was my turn to be surprised.

"All these honourable politicians are in habit of speaking in a mike. Without mike, their tummy gets bloated sir", he replied.

"No need to worry. Our honourable president shall quash their hopes. But mister home minister, why are you asking me all these?" I asked.

"You are the prime minister of this country, sir!' He looked confused.

"Oh NO, NO, NO! I do NOT want to be the prime minister", I shouted loudly.

"Wake up papa, you're dreaming", I got a push from my daughter. I woke up and found that there was a telecast of another scam. I profusely thanked God; fortunately, I am not the prime minister of this scam land!

28.11.13

*Background – In the year 2010 to 2013, many scams in public domain came into light, which led to imprisonment of some well-known politicians.*

# Eternally Late

Howrah railway station.

The platform was overcrowded. Thousands of passengers from Kolkata and nearby have gathered to catch Howrah–Mumbai Mail. The train is yet to arrive at the platform. Saurabh, my nephew has come with his luggage to catch the train to reach Nagpur for some important family event.

Clock struck 8:15 pm, departure time, but the train was nowhere in sight! Gradually time ticked away; 1, 2, 3 hrs, still the train was not in sight. There were no announcements; the officials said that they do not know about the train's status. Whole night people were stranded on the platform without any proper information about the train. Saurabh finally became tired, and unable to stay awake, he had a wink of sleep for few minutes at about 4 am

At 4:30 am, he opened his eyes and his baggage was nowhere to be seen. They were stolen. All his belongings, ticket, money, and important documents were gone. Finally the train arrived on the platform at 4:30 am, and left at 5:30 am without Saurabh, as he did not have the ticket or money.

127

The train was late by over 9 hrs. This was not an isolated event. This is happening day after day, months after months daily since last 8 months. All the trains leaving Howrah station which pass through the so-called Naxalite infested areas at night are delayed by over 8 hrs so that the trains pass through these supposedly dangerous terrains only during day time.

The authorities do not declare that the train timings have been changed and the trains will always leave after 8 hours of the scheduled time of departure. We stay in a democracy!

My daughter aged 11 years asked me, "Papa, who are naxalites? What do they look like? Are they terrible creatures?"

"No, my dear, they are humans like you and me!" I answered.

"Then who are they, papa?" the innocent child asked.

"They are educated but jobless, homeless, poor tribals who create law and order problem".

"Why is it so, papa?" again the simple question.

I looked at the ever-inquisitive child.

How can I tell her about land-mafia, mining-mafias, corruption, government apathy, swiss bank accounts of our beloved leaders whom we have voted to power?

Saturday, June 11, 2011

*Background - In 2011, there was menace of naxalites in some parts of the country obstructing movements of trains and causing law and order problem.*

# Height of Faith

"**M**ay I drink cow's urine? asked Mr Agrawal. I jumped on my chair, "What for? I asked.

"I have heard that cow's urine cures kidney failure", said Agrawal who is suffering from kidney ailment.

As a nephrologist, it is not uncommon for me to come across such funny situations but this is for the first time that I heard that cow's urine cures kidney failure!

Every moment body tissues produce wastes which are either excreted in stool, sweat, or urine. Waste and harmful chemicals produced in the tissues are poured into blood and are filtered by kidneys into urine. If these wastes are not excreted then they accumulate in the body and this is termed as kidney failure. It is most absurd to drink the same urine which is meant to be excreted out of the body. I explained these details to Agrawal, but in vain. He wouldn't listen.

"Cow's urine is sacred", said he. "It can definitely cure kidney failure"
It is easy to convince an illiterate person but quite difficult to reason with an educated person like Agrawal. So, I decided to pay him back in the same coin.

"Well, you may drink cow's urine but you must follow some basic principles to get maximum benefit. The cow must be absolutely black", I said and looked into his eyes with seriousness.

"Urine of a black cow – oh, it's easy to get!" he said.

"The cow must be a true Indian breed. I mean the ancestors of the cow must be Indian, have you understood that?" I asked.

"Obviously, sir. After all, the urine of an Indian cow has to be more sacred than a firangi cow. Even a moron can understand this simple fact" he answered, demonstrating his innate knowledge.

"And see, for best results it has to be collected on poornima (Full moon)", I added, making things more difficult for him.

To my utter surprise, he replied, "Oh, that's easy sir. Urine of a pure Indian bred, absolutely black cow collected at the midnight of Poornima". Agrawal was very happy to get an easy prescription for kidney failure.

For months I did not see him. In the meantime many poornima nights passed and one fine morning, he appeared with a sling attached to his elbow. "Good morning, sir", he said.

"Very good morning, Mr Agrawal. How are you? Ah! What has happened to your arm?" I asked with concern.

"Don't ask me", he said with an angry face.

131

"This is all due to that good for nothing ****** cow".

"Do not abuse a cow Mr Agrawal. You had said that the cows are sacred. Well, tell me, what happened?"

"See, sir, after talking to you, I searched for a pitch-black cow. It was difficult as most of them had a white or brown patch".

"Did you get such a cow?"

"Yes, I did, but family history of the cow was not very clear. In these days of adulteration, pure Indian bred cows are difficult to get".

"So, you did not get any", I gave a sigh of relief.

"I did. I went to Mathura to get one. I searched each household and with great difficulty, I got one, but it was difficult to convince the owner of the cow. Somehow the owner agreed and I took a jar and went after the cow. After all it was very precious for me".

"On poornima, I followed the cow wherever she went, but she would not oblige me. Suddenly she pissed, I ran with the jar, she got startled, turned around and in the jamboree, I slipped, injuring my shoulder and my jar of urine". He paused to take a breath.

"What happened to the jar?" I asked impatiently.

"It slipped out of my hands and all my efforts went down the drain", answered Agrawal.

"I hope you were taking the medicines prescribed by me for your kidney disease", I asked.

"Where was the time sir? In the process I forgot to take your medicines since last few months", replied the intelligent man.

05.05.2011

# Why Tie a Tie?

**43** $^0$C, it's pity to see school children attending classes in this hot summer, getting suffocated with a tie hung around their neck.

Britishers left India decades ago with some leftovers…necktie is one of them. Somehow anything related to England is considered civilised while those with our Indian culture are treated as 'primitive'. As tiny England ruled over 'uncivilised' India, the tie culture spread with 'their' civilization and soon received the status of being a 'more civilised' way of getting dressed! Even today, in many schools and colleges, dress code consists of a tie.

To tie a tie is a necessity in cold English weather. Tie prevents ice cold air from entering inside the clothing thus keeping the body warm but Indian weather is different. Here the collar of the shirt must be kept open for good ventilation to keep the body cool. Except for a few months of chilly winter, it is dreadful to tie a tie. It just throttles the throat!

Among professionals, doctors tend to be more 'tie' oriented than others without realizing that neckties have been blamed for cross infection as these are less frequently washed than other clothing. In fact, on

September 17, 2007, British hospitals published rules banning neckties. Medical representatives and those involved with sales often wear ties to impress upon customers to buy their products but the mantra for success is the quality of their product and not the tie.

There are some inherent dangers associated with tying a tie. Neckties impede flow of blood from head, thus increasing blood pressure in head and eyes. In patients of glaucoma who already have high eye pressure, a tight neck tie increases the pressure further.

Workers wearing ties while working on machineries are prone to injury if tie gets entangled. Also, in case of any accident, tie tends to obstruct free flow of air into lungs, so the first thing to do is to loosen the grip of the tie around the neck for good air flow.

In some countries like Iran, necktie is considered as a decadent symbol of European oppression. Neckties are viewed as a symbol of submission and slavery i.e., having a symbolic chain around one's neck. Britishers left India long back but left this symbol of slavery behind.

Now with advances in knowledge and technology, India is surging ahead with gusto, while England remains where it was. Tie is gradually being replaced by more rough and tough ways of dressing. In fact, the day may not be far when we shall see natives of England wearing *Kurta* rather than tying a tie around their neck, as the former becomes a mark of success and outdated tie becomes the "fashion of good old days"!

So better not to get tied to a tie!

17.05.2017

# Value of a Healthy Life

"I wish to donate my kidney", said the teenaged girl. I looked at her with surprise. She was lean-built and wheatish in complexion with dark innocent eyes. She was shy and nervous. Obviously she must have rehearsed these lines before confronting me.

"Why do you wish to donate and to whom?" I asked.

"My family is going through financial difficulty. If I get some money, family's financial crunches would be solved", said she.

"So, you wish to sell a kidney and not donate? Donation is a sacred word, do not demean it with another meaning", I told her pointedly. She did not have an answer.

Her name was Seema. I asked about her family background. She hailed from a middle class family. Her parents are farmers and had good earnings till her father took to drinking. He stopped working and started beating her mother and brother for money. Gradually all the household items were sold for purchasing liquor.

Spirituality and spirit cannot coexist. Spirit entered her home so spirituality had to leave. Soon the time came when her father had to take loans for purchasing alcohol. Farm and house were mortgaged. Children had to give up studies and started working on daily wages. This girl wished to sell her kidney to pay back the debt her father had taken. She hoped that her sacrifice would have a sobering effect on her alcoholic father.

Such people are shown the door even before I talk to them. Somehow the girl's innocence made me feel that I must help her. Selling one's organs has never helped anyone. It does not alleviate poverty nor does it help in sobering an alcoholic. Unless there is an intense desire to give up alcohol, no one can get rid of this nuisance.

"Seema, why don't you sell off one eye? You have such beautiful doe-like eyes, one is enough to see the world. You can sell off one , is not it?" Her face turned pale.

"Or do one thing, you have ten fingers, donate one of these to a person who has lost all the fingers due to accident. After all, you don't need all ten fingers. In fact we rarely use all ten fingers at any time, is not it?" She shivered at the very thought of losing her finger. "Another easy way will be to sell your one leg, it will help a limbless person to walk with support", I said.

By now, Seema was sweating profusely. She had come to earn some easy money by selling a kidney, but here the cruel doctor was suggesting her to part with her eye, finger, or a leg!

"You are feeling uneasy, Seema. You wished to sell a vital organ like kidney because you cannot see it but the very thought of losing a visible organ like a finger, eye, or leg makes you nervous."

"God has given us a beautiful life. He has gifted us with organs which can never be manufactured in a factory. Till today scientists have not been able to create even a simple cell, forget about an organ like kidney. Besides, selling an organ is not an answer to your problems."

I told Seema about our beloved late Prime Minister Lal Bahadur Shastri who was very poor. He had to walk many miles to attend  school. He used to study under the street light as his family could not afford a lantern. I also told her about Marie Curie, inventor of radium, who did her research work in a tin-shed in extremes of cold weather as she was very poor. Only hard work and determination made them overcome all the odds and turned their life around. Albeit they did not sell their kidneys to solve their problems.

I looked at Seema, I thought I could see a spark in her eyes. She slowly got up and left my chamber. There was spring in her step which was not there when she had entered.

After a few days, I saw her in a multi-speciality hospital – no, she was not admitted there for kidney surgery. She was working there as a receptionist with full honour and dignity. She smiled at me with gratitude.

Dec 17, 2006

# Hubby's Predicament

Since time immemorial, we husbands are always at the mercy of our better halves. This I learnt at *Kashi*, now Varanasi, the holy town of India and abode of lord Shiva, where I had an occasion to visit during a family get together.

*Kashi* is a land of temples. Besides famous *Vishwanath* temple, there are innumerable other temples. *Annapurna* temple dedicated to goddess Parvati is one of them. There is an interesting story behind this temple.

The story goes like this -

Once Lord Shiva said to his wife Parvati,"See how busy I am, looking after the whole world and answering prayers of my devotees, while you have nothing to do".

Parvati reasoned with him about the daily chores she has to do all day long, but Shiva wouldn't agree. This angered Parvati and feeling sad, she went away.

While Parvati was away, the whole universe faced shortage of food. People were desperate even for a handful of rice. There was famine everywhere. Parvati is considered as mother of whole universe. She felt pity for the hungry and being kind hearted, started distributing food to all at *Kashi*.

In the meantime, Lord Shiva after his meditation, felt churning in his tummy too. He went to kitchen only to find it deserted with no provision of food as his wife had left him in a fit of rage.

What to do? Shiva became desperate, with fire in his tummy and a sense of guilt for talking rough to his wife. He felt miserable. He went from house to house in search of food but he did not get any, as there was a shortage of food everywhere. Then he learnt that food is being distributed at *Kashi*. Shiva went to *Kashi*. There was a long queue for food. Shiva stood at the end of queue waiting his turn. Gradually he inched forward as the queue moved and ultimately, he reached the point where food was actually distributed. He spread his palms to receive food and looked up to see the person who was giving the food. To his surprise, he found his wife Parvati distributing the food. Moved by her kindness, he addressed her as *Annapurna*, the goddess who provides food.

Devotees at Varanasi, to worship *Annapurna*, the Goddess of food and nourishment, built a temple called *Annapurna* temple.

I sometimes wondered how come we husbands are so dependent on our spouses. After listening to this story of Devi *Annapurna*, I stopped thinking about it. If lord of lords Mahadev can be so vulnerable, then being a simple mortal man, it's not surprising that I too am vulnerable!

The vulnerability is extreme when my better half is away to her hometown Kolkata. I cannot locate my keys, clothing, cell phone, or even my socks. Every now and then I have to call her for almost everything. Somehow, she seems to know everything even when she is a thousand miles away.

"I cannot find my mobile", I said on the landline.

Without a blink, she replied back, "You have forgotten it in the bathroom while taking a bath". How did she know?!

"I lost the car keys".

"It's in your shirt pocket which you have put in the washing machine", said she. "By the way, please take out the money which you shall find in the pocket as well". I took the shirt out of the washing machine and found both the keys and the money in its pocket!

When she is away, I feel crippled and look eagerly for her return. Once she arrives, she invariably asks me, "Darling, did you miss me?"

And I answer back, "Not at all dear, not you but the Bengali sweets you must have brought!"

I wink at her. She smiles sweetly to hand over the *rosogollas* she bought for me from the land of sweets.


20.03.2020

# Colours of Life

She was a toddler who had just learnt to walk. And once she started walking, it was difficult to hold her to a single place. At one moment she was there and the very next moment she was not to be seen! She had disappeared from the scene only to be found caressing a calf in the cowshed in the courtyard. And then when her mother wanted to give her a bath, she was found to have already had a mud bath, testing the patience of her mother. She would share her food with the puppies, feeding them in plenty till her mother restrained her with wooden barricades. But the naughty baby found her own ways to climb over the barricades to free herself and play some mischief. Her favourite place was of course the bath where she would immerse herself in a tub and splash water all over till her mom noticed her and dried her with a towel. But it was just for a while. The moment her mother turned her back on her, she was back in the bath again! Gradually, as she grew up she calmed down a little.

When she was just three years old, she developed a high-grade fever. She had pink rashes all over her body and had swollen feet. Her parents took her to the Primary Health Centre and she was given some treatment. As she was not relieved of her fever, she was referred to a doctor in a nearby town. But her fever continued, her swelling increased, and a once bubbly girl became dull, lethargic, and listless. That was when the treating doctor thought of taking the opinion of a kidney specialist and the child was brought to me.

When I saw the child, she was very weak, emaciated, and barely responded to my overtures. She just opened her eyes and looked at me blankly and did not even have enough energy to slide into her mother's lap. She was burning with fever, her breathing was heavy, she was dehydrated, had marks of multiple needle pricks on both hands, and was really tired of the disease as well as of the treatments. She was moaning.

I took her frail hands in my palms. I closed my eyes. In my mind, I prayed to the almighty to help the child, "Be with me as I treat this child". In a complicated situation like this, we do need to understand the disease, we need to know about the medications and it's my belief that very often we do need more than these —blessings of the almighty.

I looked at her mother. Her worrisome face was reflecting the shadow of impending disaster. Both the parents knew that the child was in grave danger. Her father was more nervous than his wife; his eyes were swollen red with incessant tears. I have always noticed that in a crisis females are more stable and more practical as compared to their male counterparts. I started my treatment. As I put an intravenous line for the child, she barely moved her hand. I started hydrating her. Gave her necessary medications.

This has been my observation that medicines work only when the patient has confidence in them. The child was in agony and had obviously lost confidence. How do I bring this child away from her negative thoughts? How can I divert her attention from her disease and focus it on something positive?

I presented her with drawing books and colour pencils. "Shruti, I want you to draw some sketches for me". She opened her eyes with difficulty, took the presents, and gave a faint smile. As she smiled, I knew my work was half done. My magic would work.

Next day, as I did the ward rounds, her mother showed me the drawing book; it was a beautiful drawing of Lord Ganesha. Shruti was anxiously looking at me for my reaction. I smiled and exclaimed, "Oh, what a beautiful drawing! See how nice the trunk is, see that huge belly and oh, a handful of sweets! But where is the rat, the vehicle of Lord Ganesha?" Shruti smiled and enthusiastically showed me the rat drawn at the feet of the deity eating sweets. After I finished examining her, she asked what she should draw next? I told her to draw scenes of the Holi festival. My magic had started working.

The very next day, when I reached her bed, the first thing she did was show me her drawing. It was a beautifully drawn scene of Holi. Interestingly, she had used colours that were bright, indicating her state of mind, although physically she was still drained off.

She then asked for the next topic to draw. I suggested that she draw Gudi Padwa, the day of Maharashtrian new year. The next day, I found her waiting eagerly for my arrival and she showed me her drawing. "Who is this lady standing by the side of the flagpole?" I asked her. "Oh! She is my mother", Shruti replied.

What a turn of events. Earlier she used to fear me, but gradually she became my good friend to the extent that she allowed me to give her injections without any tantrums.

Every day I would suggest her a new theme to draw and she would promptly complete it on the same day. It was a task she loved to accomplish. It was not homework for her, unlike school work that most children do half-heartedly. Shruti was drawing these voluntarily, taking these tasks as challenges. Her drawings gradually improved. She improvised on her colouring. She started using water colour paints. She drew rainy days with the children going to school, herself visiting a jungle, a visit to a fair, Deepavali with lots of lamps, Jesus Christ on a cross for Christmas, Krishna carried by Vasudev through the Yamuna river for Janmashtami, a sister tying rakhi on her brother for Raksha Bandhan, a snake charmer playing a pipe in a scenery for Nag-Panchami, the national tricolor flying high on Independence Day, the peaceful Mahatma on Gandhi Jayanti, scenery of a park and much more! Soon her drawing book was full! I presented her with another drawing and painting book.

To my astonishment, I found her responding to treatment fast, her swelling started disappearing, her temperature was in control, the rashes disappeared, her cheeks became pink and life was smiling through her again.

While still in the hospital, she would draw scenery, some animals, birds, mountains, flowers, and then colour them. The colours she used were bright and vibrant. During this period, she would forget about her illness. Gradually, she improved and after a few weeks, was out of the bed. She started walking in the corridors.

Though medications did play their role in her improvement but I do believe that this child had improved quickly as she had forgotten her misery while immersed in her world of colours. For hours together she was engrossed in her coloring book. As she poured her imagination into colours, her positivity made her improve faster.

One fine day, as I was in my consulting room, a little figure peeped into my room, "Doctor uncle, see what I have drawn for you?" I curiously looked into her drawing book and burst into laughter, she had drawn me, her bespectacled, bald-headed doctor with a stethoscope hanging around his neck. "Oh naughty girl, can't you see a few hair still left on my head?" I smiled.

Shruti was ready for discharge.

6.06.2004

My Mother  Smt. Sandhya Rani Acharya

My Father  Jitendra Chandra Acharya

Great Bath at Mohenjo Daro

In the midst of ruins at Mohenjo Daro

Mahadeo temple at Karachi

Shiva idol in Mahadeo temple , Karachi

Mousoleum of Quaid e Azam , Jinnah

Supreme Court of Pakistan at Islamabad

Gunman in front of bungalow of Zulfiquar Ali Bhutto

Pak rangers in streets of Karachi

Groote Schuur Hospital at the foothill of Devils head ,
Cape Town

Jumbo chasing our car at Kruger

Bombarded remains of Railway Engine at Dimilitarized zone, Seoul, South Korea

Sculpture at DMZ showing dream of unifying Korea

Vedanta centre Prayer hall at Washington

Vedanta Centre Library, Washington

In the lap of mother nature at Bhutan

## Around the World

# In Alien Territory

During 1971 Indo-Pak war, my elder brother Captain Nilkanth had fought in the western sector. India had won a big chunk of territory in that war. In one of the villages that India won, the Pak army had abandoned an old lady aged 85 years and ran away. Indian army looked after her well and later handed her over to Pakistan with full respect and dignity. Since then I had a fascination to know about Pakistan, its land, people, and culture. So, when I got a chance to attend Congress of Asian Society of Organ Transplantation (CAST) to be held at Karachi, I grabbed the opportunity.

As we stepped into Jinnah International Airport at Karachi, we were greeted at the doorstep of the aircraft by volunteers of SIUT (Sindh Institute of Urology & Transplantation). As we stepped out of the airport and moved to our hotel, our van was followed by gun toting Pakistani rangers' vehicle from airport to the hotel. At every corner, we saw Pakistani Rangers with fingers ready on the trigger of automatic rifles. We could feel a sense of insecurity shrouded everything. Just a couple of days earlier, there was a bomb blast near the convention centre, where our conference was scheduled to take place.

The conference was well organised and was beneficial for transplant community who came from all over the globe. The organisers had taken a good care of the guests. Besides attending the conference, we also utilised this opportunity for sight seeing.

**The City of Karachi**

Karachi is the capital of Sindh province with a population of about 10 million. Earlier this province was known as Mehran. Karachi was named after Mai Kolachi, a fisherwoman.

Though advised against doing any adventure, I ventured out of the hotel and had an evening walk in the by-lanes. It's dusty with garbage dumps scattered everywhere. People in general are very poor. The vegetables are costlier than India.

We visited a few restaurants for dinner. These were all full even on weekdays. Various kinds of non-vegetarian food items were on exhibit. These included beef, lamb, fish, chicken, small and large birds etc. There is a famous restaurant called Lal Quilla (named after Delhi's Lal Quilla), which is designed like a fort. Pak President Musharraf used to visit this restaurant whenever he got time on a visit to Karachi.

162

## Mazar-e-quaid (Tomb of Quaid–e–Azam, Mohammed Ali Jinnah)

The mausoleum of Quaid–e–Azam, is the final resting place of Mohammed Ali Jinnah, the founder of Pakistan. The monument is tall and magnificent, made up of white marble with corroded bronze gates, and a chandelier of pure gold gifted by the Republic of China. The railing around the tomb is made of pure silver, a gift by the Shah of Iran, who was dethroned later.

The father of the nation of Pakistan is Jinnah. Similarity with Mohandas Karamchand Gandhi ends there. Gandhi wore inexpensive knee long khadi dhoti on a naked torso and inexpensive *chappals*. He represented an average Indian. In contrast, Jinnah was more of an Englishman than an Indian. He was very stylish - always immaculately dressed. He often wore spotless white suits. On special occasions he wore *sherwani* with white *salwar* or a *galabandh*.

While Gandhi advocated abstinence, Jinnah loved luxury. Jinnah had a wardrobe full of expensive dresses and imported shoes. His dinner table exhibited costly imported crockery. He used to smoke cigars and play golf. Jinnah used to travel in luxurious cars. He had one big 1938 model of Packard car and another 1947 model Cadillac car. These were the most expensive cars of those days. These are preserved in the museum located in the lower floor of the mausoleum. In the museum is a photograph wherein Jinnah is seen playing

163

snooker with cigar between the lips. Today majority of the common people in Pakistan can't even think of these luxuries, forget about enjoying them.

There are two shields in the museum which have the map of Pakistan printed on them. Both the maps depict the whole northeast frontier of India (i.e. part of India beyond west Bengal) included in East Pakistan. These maps also depict whole of Jammu and Kashmir and Himachal as part of West Pakistan!

## Ratneswar Mahadeo Temple at the Clifton Beach

Clifton beach is a posh area developed at the sea shore of Karachi. The beach is neat and clean. There is a Ratneswar Mahadeo temple at the Clifton beach. All religious functions are held in this temple.

## Sindh Institute of Urology and Transplantation (SIUT)

SIUT is a famous medical institute in Pakistan, founded by visionary Dr Adibul Hasan Rizvi, an urosurgeon. SIUT is the largest centre for treatment **of** kidney diseases in Pakistan. It started with eight bedded urology centres in Civil Hospital, Karachi in 1970. Now it's a huge hospital meant for nephrology, urology, and organ transplantation.

There are more than 150 hemodialysis machines, all working round the clock. Every week, 4 to 5 kidney transplantation surgeries are performed there. All the treatments including transplantations carried out in SIUT are free. Government contributes to about 30% of the expenses while rest of it is liberal donation from the people and business houses.

SIUT also houses a huge liver transplantation division. I was astonished to see that there was not a single case of alcoholic liver disease seen in that institute which is otherwise common in India. This has something to do with the Islamic religious practices in Pakistan.

## Mohenjo Daro

From Karachi, we flew in a 44 seater *Fokker* aircraft to go to Mohenjo Daro. Presently this is known as Moenjo Daro. It means mound of dead. About 2600 to 1900 BC, there existed a civilization by the bank of Indus river. For some reasons yet to be understood well, this civilization had disappeared. Later, since the time of Rigveda, 1500-1200 BC, the Gandharas had their kingdom here. History tells us that Gandhari, wife of the blind king Dhritarashtra, hailed from Gandhar. Thus, at Mohenjo Daro, we find ruins of two different ages.

R.D. Banerji, an officer with Archeological Survey of India in 1919 when he located one *stupa* at the site, discovered Mohenjo Daro. He thought it was a Buddhist *stupa*. Kashinath Narayan Dixit did major excavations in 1924.

The excavation revealed structures belonging to Gandhara period. Further exploration surprised the geologists. Below this city was a big town spread over acres of land. Carbon dating revealed that the city was nearly 5000 years old. Thus, the oldest civilization was discovered.

Detailed excavation revealed that the people of those days were highly civilised. They lived in a community, had a chieftain, and had small and big houses. There were baths and toilets in each house. Many houses were double storied. In between the houses were narrow lanes with a very advanced drainage system. The main road was 30 feet wide.

**The Great Bath**

There used to be a community bath, presently identified as the 'great bath' by geologists. The 'great bath' is a water tank, which was used by the community for bathing. The great bath is without doubt the earliest public water tank in the ancient world. It had a sloping floor made up of tightly connected tiles. At the far end of the bath was a wide *nullah* to drain used water. The floor of the tank is water tight due to finely fitted bricks laid on edge with gypsum plaster and the sidewalls were constructed in a similar manner. A series of rooms are located along the eastern edge. Most scholars agree that this tank must have been used for special religious functions where water was used to purify and renew the well-being of the bathers. The whole city of Mohenjo

Daro is testimony to the architectural mastery of the bygone era.

Farming was the main occupation of the people and their economy revolved around farm products. They also had a granary to store grains, which was well-ventilated. Besides doing farming they also made clay potteries, ornaments, and metal weapons.

The people used the river to transport their grains and other merchandise via the River Indus which flowed near the city. However, the river no longer flows close to the city now. It has drifted far away. Historians think that a big flood or the changing course of the river Indus might have been a possible cause for the destruction of this great city.

UNESCO stopped excavations in 1960 and now it has been declared a world heritage site. UNESCO, along with the archeological society of Pakistan, is now working towards conserving the excavated sites. Currently the site is threatened by ground water salinity and many of its structures are crumbling.

### Zulfikar Ali Bhutto's Town – Larkana

While going to Mohenjo Daro, we stayed at Larkana overnight. Famous for the quality of its rice, it is an important grain market and a trading centre for silk and cotton goods. Brass and other metalware are manufactured here. Larkana, named after the Larak tribe that inhabited the neighbouring area, is the birthplace of former Pakistani Prime Minister Zulfikar Ali Bhutto.

This is a district place in Sindh province. Indus River flows south of the city. Town is dusty and dirty. Roads are narrow. Traffic is chaotic and everywhere there are signs of poverty and unemployment. On our way to Larkana from Mohenjo-daro airport, we saw people traveling in carts drawn by donkeys.

This place being in Sind province has maximum Hindus. We went to a *Shakti* Temple. The temple priest told us that the Hindus and Muslims lived in peace and were very friendly. Except during the post Babri Masjid period, they never faced any difficulty. Communal strife that takes place in India is echoed in the lives of our Hindu brethren in Pakistan.

Zulfiquar Ali Bhutto, ex-Pak premier hailed from Larkana. We visited Bhutto's bungalow. The huge bungalow with sprawling lawns and swimming pool, which was once the hub of Pakistani politics, lay deserted and uncared for. Presently, the bungalow is looked after by Mr Sultan, the gun man of late Bhutto. He still guards Bhutto's house with the same diligence with which he had once guarded his life. The shadow of death hangs like a pall of gloom around the whole place. We had a snap with Sultan as a memento.

Bhutto was buried in the nearby cemetery following his capital punishment. People in general are very emotional about Zulfiquar and Benazir.

## Islamabad & Murree Hill Station

From Mohenjo Daro, we came back to Karachi to catch a flight to Islamabad. Unlike other places of Pakistan, Islamabad, the capital of Pakistan, is very neat and clean; it's a well-planned city which houses most of the foreign embassies. The Supreme Court, president's palace, prime minister's office, and Convention centre where SAARC summit was held, are magnificent in architectural design. From independence until 1967, Pakistan's capital was Karachi in the far south. Worries about the concentration of investment and development in that city are said to have led to the idea of building a new capital in a different location. During President Ayub Khan ' s tenure, a site immediately north of Rawalpindi was chosen. It was named as Islamabad.

Islamabad being up north is very cold. The temperature there was 6 degree Celsius during the day and lower at night. Rawalpindi is the twin city of Islamabad.

There are three mountain ranges in Pakistan. These are Karakorum, Hindukush, and Himalaya. Himalayan mountain range is near Islamabad. A hill station called Murree is in the Himalayan mountain range. It is 30 km northeast of Islamabad situated at 2300 metres above sea level. Like most of our hill stations, here too builders and small shops selling chips and cold drinks have spoiled the pristine landscape!

## Status of Women in Pakistan

Educational status of females in Pakistan is abysmally low which possibly suits the designs of hardcore fundamentalists in Pakistan. It appeared that Musharraf was sincerely trying to change this scenario. The females in general do not wear burka but cover their heads. Many women are seen working in the hotels and airports and other places though they all wear traditional dress and cover their heads. Even though women are venturing out of the house to work, women alone on the streets are rarely seen. Child marriages are common though illegal in Pakistan.

Law and order situation in Pakistan is awful. During my stay in Pakistan, there were disturbing reports of 'honour killings' in Pakistani press. A person killed his four daughters in order to save the family's honour by eliminating his eldest daughter, presuming that she committed adultery, and killing his remaining 3 daughters to prevent them from doing so when they grow up.

Another horrifying news published in the *Dawn* (newspaper founded by Jinnah) was that of a Hindu family. A Hindu elderly gentleman found his three daughters missing. After intensive search, he went to register a FIR with police who refused to register the case. Later he found that the girls were in the same town and had been converted into Islam by local *Mawlawi*. The burka-clad girls were allowed to meet their parents in the presence of a *Mawlawi* and said that they voluntarily embraced Islam without pressure. However, when the parents wanted to speak to the children in isolation, the *Mawlawi* refused them permission.

## Back to India

We flew back to Delhi from Islamabad via Lahore. Unlike other countries, Indians need separate visa for each province in Pakistan. We had a stopover at Lahore only for a few hours but as we did not have a visa for Lahore we could not step out of the airport. Lahore airport is a busy airport with many international flights mainly from the Middle East landing here. However, the army planes outnumber the civilian planes in Lahore airport.

As we landed in the chaotic New Delhi airport, it was a great relief for us. We did not find any gun-toting policemen around!


17.11.2006

# Cape Town - Scenic but Perilous

Cape Town is undoubtedly one of the most beautiful cities in the world. It is a port city in South Africa squeezed between the Indian and the Atlantic Ocean on a peninsula flanked by the Table Mountain. This mountain is so named because of the flat plain on its top, like a table. It is 1086 metres tall. Often a sheet of cloud covers it at the top like a white tablecloth.

There are two more mountain peaks called Lion's Head, resembling the head of a lion, and Devil's Peak. Groote Schuur Hospital, a government funded hospital where I went as a visiting doctor, is situated at the base of Devil's Peak. This hospital is the one where Christiaan Barnard did the first ever human-to-human heart transplant.

At Cape Point, the tip of the peninsula, one can see both the oceans meeting each other with the warm Indian Ocean on one side and cool Atlantic on the other. A little northeast from Cape point is a rocky headland on the Atlantic coast of Cape Peninsula known as Cape of Good Hope. Originally named Cape of Storms, it was changed to the present name because of the optimism associated with opening the sea route to India and the East. The ocean here is very stormy and has caused many shipwrecks. The sound of the stormy wind can be heard from far away.

Cape Town is a scenic, neat, and clean town full of greenery, museums and botanical gardens. The world famous Kirstenbosch National Botanical Garden is situated at the base of Table Mountain. There are many beautiful beaches like Clifton Beach with white sand. The loveliest beach of course is Boulder's Beach with thousands of penguins playing around.

There is a constant strong wind that blows in Cape Town at a speed of about 12 to 20 km per hour, which carries away all the dirt of Cape Town, making the atmosphere dust and insect free. This wind is often called 'Cape-Doctor'.

There is a ropeway that took us to the top of Table Mountain. From there we could see Robben Island situated 10 km away from the mainland. This island used to house a leper's colony in 1845 where hapless patients suffering from leprosy were kept. This was also used to keep political prisoners by the then South African Government. President Nelson Mandela was imprisoned for 17 long years on this island. This maximum security prison was closed down in 1991.

The South African society appears to be at war

with itself. It started with the war of Dutch East India Company with bushmen, Zulu and Xhosa warriors followed by the horrible bone chilling period of slavery when thousands of slaves were chained, beaten, and forced to work in most inhuman conditions, their wives raped and children abused.

Slavery stopped due to increasing costs associated with keeping of slaves and not due to moral uprising of affluent members of society. In between, there was a war between Dutch and English on one side and the French at the other. Germans also took a bite of the cake. Later, the abominable era of apartheid followed. So the times have been turbulent and full of struggle for South Africa.

There was racial discrimination till a few decades back, the facilities of social services were meant mainly for the white population. The whites who consisted only 20% of the population enjoyed 80% of the resources. They occupied the main city centres and the black population was pushed to the margins. The blacks were treated in a different section of the hospital separated from whites. White doctors treated white people only. There were separate schools, health clubs, restaurants, and even sea beaches for the whites. After sunset, if any black person was found on the road, they were jailed.

I visited Groote Schuur Hospital to learn the art and skill of deceased donor transplantation. Deceased donor transplants are very frequent in Cape Town. The hapless donors are poor black villagers who come to Cape Town for jobs, work for the whole week, and go back on Friday to their hometown for the weekend. Before departing for their villages they stop to have drinks in local pubs. As they come out, they are mugged and looted by goons in isolated places and often get killed by gunshots. Some of them are brought to the emergency room of local hospitals for treatment where they are often found to be brain dead. If no relatives come to claim the body within a day, the coroner has the power to hand over the body to the State for organ donation.

Not infrequently, there are gang wars in Cape Town. Many innocent bystanders get killed in the crossfire. These unfortunate events are heart wrenching. The law and order problems need to be braced up in this otherwise beautiful, scenic country.

During my tenure at the Groote Schuur Hospital, I had a chance to participate in Xenotransplant experiments. Xenotransplant means implanting an organ from one species to the body of another species. In Groote Schuur, pig's kidneys were removed and implanted into a baboon's body and then kidney biopsy was done serially to see whether there is any reaction to this organ.

Visit to South Africa is incomplete without a visit to Kruger National Park. The experience of wildlife was exciting and most thrilling. We entered Kruger at around 3 pm and were greeted by slender beautiful antelopes at the entry gate. As we went ahead, our guide Miss Patti got a radio message about the presence of the King of the Jungle in a distant bush. We drove there and waited near the bush for a long time and were just about to leave the place when we saw a movement behind a bush. Soon, His Excellency appeared, royal and elegant. Another followed it and they came near our car. They were so close to me that the distance between these lions and me was barely the thickness of the car window. Soon, another lion joined and went to the other side of the road, bending down to drink water from a pond by the side of the road. Later in the day, we saw warthogs, giraffes, zebras, baboons, cheetahs, elephants, and a large tortoise crossing the road. I learnt from my guide that each zebra has unique print crossings on their body, as unique as human fingerprints.

There were many baboons in that jungle. Dr Graem, my friend told me that baboons and human beings share 99% similar genes. I searched for a tail between my legs pleasantly surprised that I had none! (I must be a human then!)

As we were driving, a warthog running in the middle of the road got startled and rushed into the bushes. We were surprised to see this behaviour but soon everything became clear. There appeared a gigantic elephant very close to the road. It looked at us and then moved to the middle of the road. All of a sudden it started moving towards us at a fast pace. Its head swayed from side to side and its trunk swung wildly. It had secretions on its cheeks. Patti told us that it is a sign that the elephant is in 'heat'. Such elephants are dangerous as they can overturn vehicles and even kill men in this moment of heat.

Patti looked anxious and tried to turn the vehicle back but to her horror there were 5-6 vehicles lined up behind and a car was by the side. It was not possible to take a U turn. So she continued driving in reverse gear while the elephant continued to chase us at a fast pace. I asked Patti, why not drive past the elephant. "We shall be crushed to death if we do so!" she said. After chasing us for a kilometre or so, better sense prevailed on the elephant and it moved to the bushes.

I left South Africa with a lifetime experience filled with thrill and lots of learning.


25.12.2002

# Dine with the Dead

As I sipped tea at a busy junction in Ahmedabad, my heart was in my throat as I found myself surrounded by as many as twenty-six tombs. Yes, I was sitting in a graveyard sipping my morning tea.

Long back, when the East India Company had just started establishing its empire, Imran, an unemployed youth, was wandering aimlessly on the streets of Ahmedabad in search of a job. As he walked along the Sabarmati, he saw a few men digging graves. Fatigued, he sat down watching the gravediggers and thinking about his own survival. Just then a fakir who was passing by asked Imran for water. Imran, forgetting his own tiredness and hunger, ran around to get water for the fakir. Having quenched his thirst, the old man blessed Imran – "this place is lucky for you. Start your work at this place. You and your future generations will flourish". Blessing the young man again, the fakir – Kabiruddin left.

Imran looked around. The place was deserted except for men who came to bury their near and dear ones. What work could he start near a cemetery? – he wondered. Meanwhile, the men who had come to bury the dead had finished their work and sat down under a tree feeling tired and hungry. Imran ran around managing to get a pot, some *kulhad*, tealeaves, and milk. He then gathered some broken branches, started a fire, and made some tea for the tired men. The men blessed him and gave him a few *annas* (old coins prevalent those days). This was Imran's first earning. He had made up his mind – he would start a tea stall at that very spot.

Time passed. Imran's small tea stall continued. Fakir Kabiruddin passed away and Imran made a small mausoleum for him at the same place. The small town of Ahmedabad grew into a big city. Imran's tea-stall, which was on the outskirts of a small town, now found itself in the middle of a growing city. The cemetery was no longer used; many shops got established around it. Imran continued to sell tea. He barricaded the tombs with steel railings, beautified the place, replaced the rusty benches with chairs and tables, and added snacks to his menu. He named his tea stall as 'Lucky Restaurant'.

Today Imran is no more but business continues. His great grandsons now run Lucky Restaurant and they are doing a roaring business from dawn till midnight right in the heart of busy Ahmedabad. Waiters clean these graves each morning and pay their respect with offerings of fresh flowers.

If you happen to be in Ahmedabad, do not forget to sip tea or dine with the dead at Lucky Restaurant situated at *Lal Darwaza* area of Old Ahmedabad city. The tomb of saint Kabiruddin still stands by the side of the restaurant. This is world's only tea stall built on a cemetery!

10.02.2018

# Mission of Peace at Washington

In 1893, Swami Vivekanand visited Chicago where he had delivered a speech in World Parliament of Religions. After almost a century, Ramkrishna Math was established at Washington DC as Vedanta Centre. It was interesting to see Ramkrishna Math Ashram in USA established by monks of American origin who were highly motivated by Vedanta philosophy. Interestingly, these monks used to practice and still have respect for different religions like Judaism and Christianity.

It all started with Swami Shobanand Maharaj, who established Ramkrishna Math at Hollywood, the first Math in America. He was of the view that Washington DC, being the capital of USA, must have a Vedanta centre. As they looked for a place to start the centre, they came across an old dilapidated house, which was purchased by contribution from followers of Shri Ramkrishna, teacher of Swamy Vivekananda. The place was in the midst of woods. Disciples gave voluntary service and cleared the jungle to start a small temple of Shri Ramkrishna. They started a small library there. Disciples would gather to listen to the philosophy of Vedanta, gospels of Shri Ramkrishna and messages of Swamy Vivekananda. As there was no proper place to sit in ice-cold winters, they would set up tent for devotees to gather. Thus this centre started in 1985.

Soon three monks came together and religious discourses were regularly held. Gradually, local Americans came to know about Vedanta and started flocking to the centre. As per the direction of the Ramkrishna Mission, Belur Math, no donations were asked by the monks but people voluntarily contributed. A local architect became interested in the Ashram, made a blueprint, and soon the Vedanta centre took its magnificent present form.

The centre today has a big prayer hall where the bust of Shri Ramkrishna which was brought from India is installed. Attached to it is a nice library where spiritual literature is kept for disciples to read. In the basement there is a hall where lectures and classes are organised. There is a fountain in the courtyard, a small pond, garden, and parking space. In the basement a kitchen has been made for cooking community meals on different occasions.

Besides the birth anniversary of Shri Ramkrishna, mother Sharada and Swamy Vivekananda, Durga Pooja and Christmas festivities are also celebrated here.

There are three Swamyjis looking after the centre. Swamy Atmagyanananda is the head Swamiji. Swamy Bramharoopananda and Swamy Chidambarananda assist him. They take turn in taking classes for the devotees on daily basis besides conducting the religious activities. As I took a tour of the centre, I came across beautiful paintings of Swamy Vivekananda, Ma Sharada and Shri Ramkrishna painted by the devotees of the centre.

I was fortunate to have a talk with Swamy Bramharoopananda of this centre. He said that with people's cooperation, they did not have any difficulty in starting the centre. Swamy Bramharoopananda originally is from Karnataka and was a professor in philosophy. His parents wanted him to get married and settle but his inclination towards spirituality brought him close to Swamy Sabanandaji of Hollywood who instructed him to join Washington centre.

When asked about any message for youth of India, he said, "Be strong, develop yourself, and serve". The same words spoken by Swamy Vivekananda.

He was happy about the state of women in India but said that much more needs to be done. "We consider women as the embodiment of Divine Mother. They must be given respect, education, and should be free from any exploitation. A civilization is judged by the way it treats its women".

12.09.2019

# Demilitarised Zone of Korea

S outh Korea has been described as the 'Land of Morning calm' because of its spellbinding natural beauty of picturesque high mountains, clear waters, and splendid tranquility. But this tranquility has been lost due to constant friction between the two nations – North and South Korea.

After the outbreak of the Korean War, which claimed millions of lives, De-Militarised Zone (DMZ) was created. DMZ is the only land boundary between South and North Korea. Though this zone separating the North and South Korea is demilitarised, the border beyond that strip is one of the most heavily militarised borders in the world. Both North and South Korea maintain Peace Villages on each other's side of DMZ. The inhabitants of the villages Tae Sung Dong to the South and Kijōng-dong to the North are known as Peace Villages. The villagers are direct descendants of people who lived there before the Korean War and are protected and governed by United Nations Command.

The DMZ is 250 km long and 4 km wide and the Han River flows through this area. This isolation of the heavily landmined DMZ has created a natural reserve and several endangered flora and fauna exists in this fortified place.

I had a chance to visit South Korea in 2019 to meet my daughter Jaya who studied there in Chonnam National University as an international exchange student at Gwangu. Our first stop was the Imjingak Park and the Freedom Bridge, which was built as a memorial to the war days and a tribute to the separated families. Between 1974 and 1990, the South Koreans crossing the DMZ discovered four tunnels. The tunnels were created for military invasion on Seoul. These are 73 metres deep and run for more than one and half kilometres. Each tunnel has a width and height of two metres. Today these tunnels have been closed using multiple concrete walls and we can view the tunnel using a sloped access shaft. South Koreans believe there may be more tunnels yet to be discovered. This is a reminder of the continued tension between North and South Korea.

In the Imjingak Park many memoirs of the devastating Korean War are kept. A railway engine is one of them, which is badly damaged due to bombarding.

After visiting the third tunnel we were on our way to the Dora observatory. Situated on top of the Dora Mountain we could see the actual border between the two Koreas, the Peace village on either side of the border, the flagpoles and the Han River.

Our final stop was at the Dorasan railway Station. A station which sits on a railway line which once connected the North and the South, a station where the train is ready but it does not get permission to cross the line, a station where there is hope of reunification and a dream to build a line connecting Korea through China and Russia to Europe. There is a nice sculpture showing two halves of the world being united by common people dreaming that one day both South and North Korea will unify.

After the Korean War, South Korea was one of the poorest countries of the world. In just two generations, it has become a developed and rich nation and is still a fastest growing developed country. It has a highly motivated and educated population rich in advanced technology and export-oriented economy.

Visit to Korea is incomplete without the mention of its culinary expertise, which is sure to titillate taste buds, and the fashion streets with many beauty shops and clinics for facial plastic surgeries.

Seoul has many well-maintained old fortresses depicting its glorious past. Even today, change of guards ceremony in these fortresses is a big attraction and worth seeing. There are many temples dedicated to Lord Buddha. But somewhere the message of peace by Buddha has gotten lost. I earnestly wish that long lost peace should return in this land of morning calm.

6.06.2019

# Social Articles

# Let Us Put Their Shoes On

When there is a flame in the belly, the mind sets on fire first.

With the ongoing crisis of COVID and migration of labourers from metropolises to villages, there appears to be a big setback for the epidemiologists who fear unprecedented health crisis and tragedy of a magnitude beyond imagination. Why do the labourers flee from town to villages? Don't they realise the tragedy looming large to affect them, their families and their neighbourhood? There has been constant governmental and social messaging all over the country about the lurking danger of COVID, which does not differentiate between rich, poor, young, old, male, female, employee, employer, religion, or faith.

Why then, are the labourers fleeing with their families, including small kids and the elderly, in this hot summer, while being fully aware that the facilities in villages are miniscule as compared to the towns?

Let us put ourselves in their shoes and feel the pinch. The place of work and accommodation for labourers in towns are mostly small and dingy. There is a shortage of food. If they go out of their house in search of a job, they meet the police ready to strike with batons. Regretfully, at first, it was fun to look at from the comfort of our own cosy homes.

The employers, themselves not rich, are in debt with loans from the bank and other sources. It is not possible for them to continue paying salaries with all businesses closed. They themselves have no income. The employers can absorb the cash crunch only for a limited period. It will be impossible to pay salaries without any income.

When a crisis strikes, it is but natural to think about our home where our loved ones live. "Even if I die, let me be with my loved ones", "I shall never come back to this dreaded town again", or "What is happening to my dear ones in the village?" are the questions which arise in everyone's mind.

Hunger, cries of children, and the cruel heat of summer all add to the woes, and if there comes a situation where sick or pregnant ladies are in the family, the mind gets disturbed easily, unable to accept sound reasoning of authorities.

Labourers need food, safety, and the assurance of a reasonable future for themselves and their families. With the present doles brought out by the government wherein billions of dollars are being pumped to revive the economy, we hope that this migration will stop, shutters will be lifted, and the people will return to their work immediately, while maintaining a social distance and observing work ethics strictly. Spitting, loitering, gathering for marriages, festivities, crowding in malls, cinemas, gyms, or swimming pools invite health hazard and this realisation should dawn into the lifestyle of everyone for months to come.

The health structure is in shambles. Barely 1.28% of the GDP is being spent on health (in the year 2019). It is time to strengthen this basic facility. All educational institutes need to be spruced up to start the season with facilities of hand hygiene and masks. Educationists need to think about utility of continuing present education system or to change it to a more practical one, useful at times of crisis.

All religious organisations also need to focus on their modus operandi and stress upon building up values and making bonds of friendship and love.

Every dark cloud has a silver lining. This unprecedented COVID crisis serves as a wake-up call for all of us.

## 25.05.2020

*Background – In 2020, following the pandemic of Corona virus, India clamped lockdown to contain its spread. There was a mass exodus of labourers from cities back to their villages.*

# Spirit to Keep Spirits High!

When spirits are low, sprinkles of spirit can soar it high! So, it is nothing unusual for the state government running with low spirit to remember spirit at such depressing moments.

What message does this send to the society? The government has been elected to take care of the well being of the society. Anything that it does is a step towards building up a good, morally high, healthy society. But if the government has opened up the liquor shops, is it still for the good of its citizens?

With businesses getting ruined and markets biting the dust, with coffers being empty and expenses abysmally high, those in power turn towards the age-old companion of the human race – alcohol.

It is claimed that alcohol will alleviate the economy of the state! Multiple calculations have been brought forth to support the opening of liquor shops.

The basic question here is whether alcohol really helps the economy or destroys it? As a person gulps alcohol, it not only enters his belly but also his brain. The ability to differentiate between good and bad is lost. One predictable outcome is graph of crime rates touching the sky.

A few sips of alcohol in the tummy and reflexes get delayed causing accidents that invite injury and untimely deaths. We are all witness to the fact that traffic accidents have decreased considerably during this lockdown. With liquor shops opening, we will have to face these avoidable tragedies again.

The most devastating effect of alcohol, however, is domestic violence. Men beat their wives and children, avoid going to work because of alcohol's after-effects, and sell household items to buy alcohol.

Alcohol disrobes man of his propriety. Morality goes down the drain and prostitution is the outcome. Who suffers? Sufferers are mostly innocent women who do not touch alcohol.

Government is giving free rice, wheat, and lentils to the poor for them to survive but it's not giving alcohol for free. In fact, alcohol is being sold at a higher tariff. To purchase alcohol, the same food items received for free will be sold in the market to purchase alcohol!

Our elected representatives are the guardians of society and are supposed to look after the health of the people. Does alcohol improve health or does it denigrate it? Alcohol causes many ill effects, including gastritis, jaundice, and progressive liver damage. I have seen alcohol ruining innumerable families. Rich people have become poor, businesses have been ravaged, and ancestral property has been sold at throwaway prices besides the family honour touching all time low because of this dreadful addiction.

While counting the revenues from alcohol, the leadership forgot to look at the other half of the balance sheet – the part showing the expenses. The money lost for absenteeism from work, traffic accidents, domestic violence, ruining of work force due to addiction, crimes committed under influence of liquor, prostitution, expenses incurred for treating people with liver failure, and much more. Are these not enough to derail the economy?

No amount of financial gain can make up for the immense human tragedy that is inflicted by liquor. It will be wise on the part of government to dump this idea of opening liquor shops and delivering liquor at the doorstep of common man under the disguise of economic resurrection!

8.06.2020

*Background – In 2020, following the pandemic of Corona virus, India clamped lockdown to contain its spread. State governments facing financial crunch allowed liquor sales.*

# Kidney Health for Everyone Everywhere

Kidneys are called great sweepers of the body. Imagine all sweepers going on strike for a day, the whole city will collapse with dirt and diseases in no time. But we now realise that kidneys are more than just sweepers; besides cleaning dirt from blood they also maintain haemoglobin, blood pressure, and make bones strong. They also play a vital role in keeping the heart strong.

Children and the elderly are more prone to kidney damage. Repeated urine infection in children may indicate a serious ailment in which some amount of urine flows back into the kidneys during micturition instead of going out, thus damaging the kidneys gradually. The Elderly lose kidney function with advancing age.

High blood pressure and diabetes can quietly damage kidneys for years before symptoms develop. Fortunately, with lifestyle changes and treatment, one can reduce the risk of life-threatening complications. High blood pressure is both a cause and result of kidney disease.

Interestingly, we tend to damage kidneys unknowingly due to faulty lifestyles with addictions like tobacco in any form (*Gutka*, pouches, *kharra*, and cigarettes), bad eating habits, and lack of exercise leading to obesity. Obesity is an excess of body fat resulting in a significant impairment of health and longevity. Excessive food intake and inactivity is the main reason for developing obesity.

Obesity is dangerous. Diabetes, hypertension, heart disease, arthritis, liver disease, cancers, kidney stones, psychological, and sleep disorders are associated with obesity. Chronic kidney disease is three times more common in obese individuals.

Whatever we eat gives us energy or calories. Different foodstuff has different energy value, for example 100 grams of cucumber has 15 calories but 100 grams of *jalebi* has 300 calories. Also once ingested, *jalebi* gives instant energy while cucumber takes more time to get assimilated, as it is rich in fibres.

Earlier, obesity used to be a sign of prosperity limited to affluent class, but now we consider it as a sign of physical inactivity, because obesity is seen even in poor and middle-class people.

The ancient proverb, "breakfast like a king, lunch like a prince, and dine like a pauper" holds true for all. If you wish to enjoy life, just shed a few pounds!

Taking painkillers and drugs containing metallic salts are potential poisons that damage kidneys.

Females are vulnerable to kidney damage during and immediately after pregnancy or abortion.

Farm labourers working in extremes of temperature without provision of proper drinking water are prone to chronic kidney disease. Use of insecticides and hard water could be a cause of such kidney damage.

Kidney disease often creeps in like a thief without any obvious symptoms. Unexplained tiredness, bony pains, irregular menses, infertility, lack of interest in sex, nausea, vomiting, frothing of urine, swelling of feet, and puffy face, itching, inability to concentrate are few subtle symptoms which are often ignored.

Simple inexpensive urine and blood tests can reveal kidney damage. Presence of even a small amount of protein in urine can predict kidney disease. Sonography of abdomen can be a next step.

In extreme cases of kidney failure, filtration of blood (Dialysis) or kidney transplantation can be done; both options are now available widely. But why wait till then, prevention is better than cure.

Prevent kidney disease with healthy habits, exercise, avoid obesity, avoid pain killing drugs, keep blood pressure and sugar under check, and drink cnough water.

14.03.2019

# Does Religion Prohibit Organ Donation?

"**M**y religion is very simple. My religion is kindness".- Dalai Lama

All the religions around the world have emphasised on the importance of love, charity, sympathy, and empathy. Donation of food, alms, cows, and land has been well documented in religious scriptures. Donating part of one's own body to a suffering needy person is the noblest action.

In *Mahabharata*, an incidence is mentioned wherein Karna donated his life-saving *Kavach* knowing well that this would cause his death in the battle.

No religion is against organ donation. Centuries ago, when the religious scriptures were written, blood or organ donations were not invented but these have become a reality today. So, we need to focus on stretching the spirit of donation to organ donation to save lives.

There are certain religious groups which believe that God created them as a whole and they prefer to return to Him as a whole. With this belief, many people bury amputated limbs, foreskin from circumcision, amnion, and placenta after delivery. These beliefs also prevent them from organ donation.

In Islam, religious leaders, *'ustazs'*, *'ulamas'*, and *mufti* have different interpretations on organ donations, but all agree that the holy book Koran does not forbid tissue donation.

*Mufti* is an expert in Islamic law qualified to give authoritative legal opinions known as *fatwas*. Muftis are appointed by government to deal with Islamic matters. *Fatwas* are religious rulings made by *'Fatwa Committee'* on various issues. *'Fatwa* Committee' chaired by a *mufti* includes prominent religious leaders, lawyers, doctors, and other members of public. *Fatwas* are not legally binding. Often these religious leaders have come out with *fatwas* to donate organs. But despite *fatwas*, people are often reluctant to donate organs.

A religious practice that often comes in the way of organ donations among different communities is that a body must be buried as soon as possible after death – the sooner the better, usually less than 8 hours. Often because of procedural delays in carrying out organ donation, it is not possible. With cooperation of officials, this delay is avoidable.

Christianity promotes organ donation. Pope John Paul II stated that "we shall receive our supreme reward from God according to the genuine and effective love we have shown to our neighbor". The Bible states, "Give, and it will be given to you. A good measure, pressed down, shaken together and running over, will be poured into your lap. For with the measure you use, it will be measured to you". (Luke 6:38).

The attitude of Buddhism is in perfect agreement with organ and tissue donation; in Buddhist Scriptures there are stories where donation of tissues have been referred to as an act of charity earning merits. In the Sutra of Golden Light, a Mahayana Sutra, Buddha in a previous lifetime as a young prince is said to have encountered a starving tigress and her cubs and killed himself to provide her with food.

What is important for a Buddhist at the time of death is not the condition of their body but of their mind. A state of non-attachment to the body is desirable at this time. This can be aided by the generosity involved in deciding that after death, one's body or its parts can be used to help others.

There are many people suffering from kidney, liver, lungs, or heart failure whose lives can be saved if these failing organs are replaced. In India, every year 1-1.5 lakh kidneys are needed in the country but only about 5000 are transplanted. At the same time 15,000-20,000 livers are required every year but only 500 are transplanted. If people donate the organs after death then these shortages will be overcome and many lives can be saved.

We must realise that the concept of brain death is a reality today. Once a person's brain is dead, they cease to survive.

As I leave this transient world
Let me kindle a ray of hope
In the eyes of those
Who can't see,
A breeze of fresh air for those
Who can't breathe,
An elixir of life for them
Whose kidneys have failed,
Let my heart beat in those
Whose heart is fluttering to stay alive.

13.08.2016

# Eyes, the Most Divine Gift

Out of all the six senses the most divine one is vision – we see the beautiful creation of the master crafter because of our eyes. The very thought of blindness sends chills down the spine.

In Indian mythology, there is mention of Dhritarashtra , the king of *Kaurava* clan who was born blind. Not to be looked upon as a better half, his wife Gandhari did penance by tying a piece of cloth on her eyes. He ruled the kingdom but problems occurred not because of blindness but because he had lost his inner vision too, the ability to look inside oneself. The war of *Mahabharata* was a result of lack of insight rather than out-sight.

*Mahabharata* also mentions about divine vision gifted to Sanjay, a trusted charioteer of Dhritarashtra by Vyasa Rishi, who could see the happenings at the warfront the way we see television nowadays. Lord Krishna blessed Arjuna with divine eyes so that he could see the divine universal form of the lord.

In 11th century, eyes of the great Rajput King Prithviraj Chauhan were burnt with red hot iron rod by his tormentor Sultan Shahbuddin Muhammad Ghori who was earlier defeated by Prithviraaj Chauhan, but was set free as a gesture of mercy. Ghori attacked for a second time next year. Prithviraj was defeated and captured at the Second Battle of Tarrain (1192). Ghori did not show any mercy, he took Prithviraj to Ghazni and blinded him. As per history, directed by poet Chand Bardai through a poem, Prithviraj killed Mohammad Ghori by a single arrow.

In 15th century blind saint, poet, and musician, Surdas composed devotional songs dedicated to Lord Krishna. Surdas is said to have written and composed a hundred thousand songs in his magnum opus the '*Sur Sagar*' (Ocean of Melody), out of which only about 8,000 are extant. He has described the beauty of Kanha, young Krishna, in such a meticulous way as if he could see lord Krishna in reality!

To donate eyes after death is the most divine gift I can think of. Those who have lost vision due to any reason can see the divine world again if given this precious gift. As such after death our physical body has no pain and is of no use to us, then why not to give this parting gift to someone who really needs it!

17.11.2013

# Burn Your Greed, Not Your Brides

Since time immemorial we have heard of bride burning. In Hindu mythology, the first encounter is that of Sita entering the lit pyre in order to prove her chastity while Rama, her husband, looks on without any attempt to desist her from doing so.

In Mahabharata, we come across Madri performing sati after death of her husband Pandu as she blamed herself for his death.

We have heard about 'jauhar'. Whenever Rajput Kings went to war and winning seemed a distant dream, the womenfolk would jump into the pyre dressed in wedding finery to protect themselves from Muslim invaders.

Even as recently as 125 years ago, 'Sati pratha' was followed wherein wives used to immolate themselves by jumping into the pyre of their dead husbands, becoming a Sati. More often the hapless wives were forced to become Sati. This was outlawed by the British Empire due to efforts of Raja Rammohan Roy in 1829. He was motivated by the experience of seeing his own sister-in-law being forced to commit sati. He visited Calcutta cremation grounds to persuade widows against immolation and formed watch groups to do the same.

Following the outcry after the sati of Roop Kanwar, the Indian Government enacted the Rajasthan Sati Prevention Ordinance in 1987. The Prevention of Sati Act makes it illegal to abet, glorify, or attempt to commit sati. Abetment of sati, including coercing or forcing someone to commit sati. Doing so can be punished by death sentence or life imprisonment, while glorifying sati is punishable with 1–7 years in prison.

However, even today bride burning is not uncommon in India. Invariably this is a result of greed of in-laws who demand dowry. Often the culprits are females themselves – sisters and mothers-in-law who torture poor brides and burn them as the bride's family is unable to fulfill their demands. It is surprising that news of bride burning often comes from affluent families and not from poor homes.

In Gita, Lord Krishna has said that there are three gates to hell - greed, lust, and anger. Both greed and lust are insatiable. Leo Tolstoy had written a story 'How much land does a man need'. Truly he needs only three by six feet of land to be buried, but he often dreams of an empire.

For how long will our society suffer from this evil? Is it not time to change our attitude towards our better halves? Should we not look upon them as human beings rather than as a commodity?

Let us spread a message to the society, "Burn your greed, not your brides".

25.02.2012

*\* Dowry deaths reported in some parts of country in 2011*

# Defining Death!

When a person is declared as dead, all eyes turn to the ECG monitor for a flatline. But a person can still be alive despite his ECG showing a straight line! Conversely, there are situations where heart is beating, pulse and blood pressure is maintained but still the person is dead! The latter occurs in the background of severe head injury or brain hemorrhage. Then the question arises, when do we call a person dead?

There are situations like cardiac surgery where the heart is artificially kept at a standstill, it's not beating but the person is alive! In case of heart transplantation, heart of the patient is removed and a healthy heart is put inside. So, for a certain period, the person does not have heart to beat, but still he is alive! Once he comes out of anaesthesia, he starts moving his body, begins breathing, and thus shows signs of life. So if stoppage of heart is not death, then what is it that differentiates a live person from a dead one?

In the brain there is an area called brain stem that controls vital functions like breathing. Damage to this area causes loss of consciousness and breathing stops. The oxygen supply to this area is crucial. Irreversible damage to brain stem causes irreversible loss of consciousness and a person stops breathing. Ultimately, blood pressure falls and heart stops. This is called Brain Stem Death, which is 'actual death' as it is irreversible.

Worldwide, two distinct mechanisms of death are recognised; namely irreversible cardiopulmonary arrest i.e., stoppage of heartbeat, and breathing and Brain Stem Death (BSD) or Brain Death (BD). The key feature of both mechanisms is irreparable brain damage. The two mechanisms differ only because death is diagnosed in the presence or absence of a beating heart. Unfortunately, the public normally associates death with cardiac standstill i.e., stoppage of heart.

Although the brain relies on the heart to circulate oxygenated blood, machines can replicate this function. In contrast brain function cannot be artificially replaced and the heart always stops within days or weeks of the brain stem dying. So death of a person is actually a brain stem death.

12.02.2010

## Lest They be Forgotten

# Purushottum Dr G. M. Taori

 Few of our colleagues had a discussion on who could fit in the category of *'Purushottum'* (Best among men) in today's scenario. The only person we could think of was Dr Girdhar Madangopalji Taori.

Besides being a neurologist *par excellence*, he was a humanist to the core. He was a visionary who thought of an institute devoted to neurology and developed it without compromising with values.

I met Dr. Taori in 1983 while I was preparing for my MD thesis topic on psychomotor epilepsy. Expecting to meet a big person, I entered his chamber nervously with a palpitating heart. Seated there was a thin simple looking man wearing a hand shirt. The room was just as simple as the man. Dr. Taori guided me and answered my queries in a simple language. His simplicity remained unchanged throughout his life.

The very next year in 1984, this simple man took an extraordinary and courageous step. He established Central India Institute of Medical Sciences (CIIMS) almost at the far end of the then Nagpur. CIIMS was the first ever super specialty hospital in a private setup, exclusively devoted to neurology. It took 11 years to get permission for this hospital from civic authorities due to bureaucratic red tape. Ultimately he had to write to the then Prime Minister Mrs Indira Gandhi. The going was not so smooth though. CIIMS faced many hurdles posed mainly by its own employees, but with apt handling by Dr Taori, these were overcome.

He devoted his every moment, his every thought, and every penny in the development of CIIMS. He was far from pomp and show. He never differentiated between rich and poor. Once, a person who donated a large sum of money for this hospital said that even for the donors the facility and priorities are same as any poor patient.

Trained in Christian Medical College, Vellore, and Canada, the vision of Dr Taori was to develop CIIMS as a teaching and research oriented ethical institute besides treating patients. The National Board recognised CIIMS for Diplomate (DNB) courses. No students had to give donations to get DNB seats in CIIMS. CIIMS research wing has come out with cheap and easy tests to diagnose causative organisms in meningitis.

His desire was to build a rehabilitation centre for the disabled, which he could not fulfill due to lack of space and finances.

I was among the fortunate few who were in the good books of Dr Taori. He had graced our annual programme of Academy of Medical Sciences as a chief guest. In his deliberation he talked about ethics in medical practice.

211

In the last week of his life I was called to see him. I touched his feet, sat besides him holding his tremulous hands. He narrated his history and was very clear about the treatment he needed. His heart had gone weak and kidneys were affected. He had realised that the sands of time were slipping fast through his fingers, his end would come very soon but he faced it courageously.

The last few hours of Dr Taori were very significant. He called all the members of CIIMS and guided them about what to do in the future, thanked the nurses and doctors who took care of him during his illness, and told the intensivists not to put any endotracheal tube (tube in the throat). Lastly, he called the senior doctors of CIIMS and said his last words 'sabko saath lekar chalo' (take everyone along).

CIIMS was his ultimate desire, dream, and passion. He was fully devoted to this institute and ultimately his last breath was also in CIIMS.

Truly, Dr.Taori was a karmayogi.

I remember a poem by Walt Whitman who penned these verses on the death of Abraham Lincoln, which fit perfectly for Dr G. M. Taori too:

"O Captain! my Captain! our fearful trip is done,
The ship has weather'd every rack, the prize we sought is won,
The port is near, the bells I hear, the people all exulting,

While follow eyes the steady keel, the vessel grim and
daring;
But O heart! heart! heart!
O the bleeding drops of red,
Where on the deck my Captain lies,
Fallen cold and dead."


19.06.2015

# Dr. Balswaroop Chaubey

With Dr Balswaroop Chaubey's demise, an era of clinical medicine came to an end. He was a beloved teacher among students and a darling doctor for the patients. He shaped careers of hundreds of his students. Many of his students are doing well in various fields of medicine spread across the world.

Way back in 1982, I was posted in psychiatry as a junior resident. Dr Chaubey was the head of the Department of Medicine. One fine day I was instructed by Dr Chaubey to join the team of intensive care unit. With that posting, my life changed. As a resident of ICCU, we used to work day and night, all the days of the week without any break. Even on the night of Deepawali when others went for celebrations, we worked. The experience of working in ICCU is helping me till today. I remain indebted to Dr Chaubey for this.

Dr Chaubey was known for his flash diagnosis and clinical acumen. He could see what others could not. Once in our ICCU, a young boy aged about 16 years was admitted with irregular heartbeat. He was put on multiple drugs to stabilise his heartbeat but the beats remained irregular. Next morning when Dr Chaubey was taking rounds, he wondered why a young boy is admitted in ICCU. He was told about irregular heartbeats resistant to all drugs. Dr Chaubey asked the boy to open his mouth and saw tobacco inside. He instructed us to stop all drugs and told the boy to give up chewing tobacco. After few hours, patient's heartbeat normalised without any drugs!

On another occasion, we had an old man admitted with diarrhoea and irrelevant behaviour. He had been recently discharged from the mental hospital. Dr Chaubey saw the patient from a distance and noticed skin changes. He diagnosed Pellagra and advised him to be treated with vitamins. The patient who has been suffering for years was cured in no time. There are such innumerable instances in which even without blood tests or costly investigations he diagnosed diseases. This was because of his basic simple clinical approach. I have never seen him talking about big syndromes or costly investigations. Of course, during those days even simple tests like ultrasonography were not available.

He always wore a smile besides a long white apron. Patients treated him like a god. While he was very kind to the patients, he was equally strict with the students and his subordinates. Once, in the middle of night at about 3 am, I found sweepers cleaning and wiping the floor in front of ICCU. I was wondering that how this change of attitude has occurred among sweepers and attendants. They answered, "Dean *saheb* is coming to ICCU to see a patient".

Often, he would spring a surprise by appearing from nowhere when he was least expected. Once at about 11 pm, I was by the side of central monitor in ICCU. As I turned around, I found him standing next to me. We did not expect the head of the hospital visiting at that late hour. While taking rounds I often saw him humming.

At the fag end of his life, he was awarded *Padmashree*. He got a congratulatory message from Dr G.S. Sainani, his contemporary, that the other persons awarded with him include Aishwarya Rai and Akshay Kumar. Dr Chaubey smiled and said jocularly that it would be better to act in films and get recognition early than to toil among patients and remain unrecognised. During his felicitation he said, "A teacher is like sandpaper and student a pencil. Sand paper makes the student sharp but does anyone realise what happens to the sand paper?"

He was once invited to the inaugural function of a multi-specialty hospital. Dr Chaubey made a sharp comment, "Buildings made of cement and sand does not make a hospital, you need doctors to make a hospital". He was also sad about the present state of medical teaching. "The commercialisation of medical teaching is killing the clinician while making a doctor", he had commented.

Today, with Dr Chaubey's demise, I feel a big vacuum, an emptiness that I cannot describe. He was a father figure to many of us, a guiding lighthouse. He shaped the career of many of us without us realizing that the master has worked his magic on us.

21.11.2011

# Dr Vikram Marwah

 Dr Vikram Marwah was an academician, laureate, a selfless doctor, and a great human being. The list remains incomplete without the word 'sculptor' for he not only shaped the careers of many doctors but also actually carved many surgical appliances.

My first meeting with him was during the annual social gathering as a first year medical student in 1976 when he was the dean of Government Medical College, Nagpur. We were new to medical school, full of anxiety due to the fear of ragging..

Dr Marwah saw us from a distance and came to us. He distributed sweets with his own hands to first year students. I am yet to see such generosity from a dean of a medical college anywhere else. "Students will eat first, as a dean I shall be the last person to take a bite", he had said.

We students had organised *Saraswati Pooja* in the campus. He not only attended the *pooja* but also recited a few poems of Rabindranath Tagore. He was fluent in Bengali.

He was a prolific writer. He wrote stories related to his life experience as a doctor. When my book *'Kathputaliyan'* was released, after about a week, I went to present him my book. By that time he had already borrowed the book from one of his students and finished reading. He discussed few of the stories of the book and encouraged me to write more.

Exposure in his father's workshop, and the wave of patriotism that had swept the nation when he was studying in Kolkata in the early forties, had a tremendous influence on his life.

I call him an artist and sculptor. He loved to experiment with surgical instruments. During his time, surgical instruments were scarce and costly. With few alterations, he made new inventions, which were cheap and durable. He developed many orthopaedic appliances as per the need of his patients. He told me a story about how he used a simple fan used as an exhaust to keep the OT clean and smell-free. Another fascination of his was cars. He could refurbish old cars and use them.

He devoted his post retirement period in the service of humanity in *Matru Seva Sangh*. He operated upon hundreds of polio-afflicted children free of charge.

He was president of *Vishwa Punar Nirman Sangh* (VPNS) and was also founder of the trust running

219

*Bharti Krishna Vidya Vihar* School with the aim to develop character among the students. He actively participated in the school programmes till he was forced to shelve his gloves due to failing health.

We had invited him to the platform of Academy of Medical Sciences where he spoke on '*Down the memory lane, the past and present of medical profession*'. We were glued to our seats due to his oratory skills.

He had devoted his life to the service of humanity. He could reach the poorest of poor and did not differentiate between powerful and underprivileged.

We shall miss him forever – a lovely human being that he was!

7.11.2013

# Remembering Dr Popatlal H. Soni

Dr Popatlal Harakchand Soni was a dexterous surgeon; his fingers were like magical instruments. He has taught three generations of surgeons. He had a different way of teaching. He was upright and honest. His answers to any questions were straightforward. His students loved and respected him for his knowledge and teaching style. Soni sir's clinical notes were very famous among his students. These were the compilation of his teachings by his students, which he taught by the bedside of patients.

I was lucky to be one of his students. He was friendly with his students. I remember, we all students would surround him after the tutorial class and ask him a lot of questions. He used to answer them very patiently. He was very cool in the operation theatre and deftly dissected tissues almost similar to what is shown in textbooks. He used to encourage his students to study and analyze clinical challenges.

Once he told me, "Study...Or else you shall be of nowhere"'. I wrote it on cardboard and placed it on my study table. This sentence of his had encouraged me from time to time whenever I faced difficulties.

A parent of a medical student once approached Dr Soni through an acquaintance to pass his ward in the final MBBS examination. Dr Soni replied, "Yes I can pass this student, but if he is not efficient enough to pass by himself then we shall be sending an incompetent doctor to the society, will it not be harmful? Let the student study well and pass on his own merit". The person was speechless after hearing this frank reply. Dr Soni never compromised on principles.

Innumerable patients have benefitted by his treatment. Patients considered him their own family member. Often, they would approach him for social problems unrelated to the field of medicine. Surely, we shall always miss this great surgeon, nice human being, and an extraordinary teacher.

7.02.13

# Benevolent Dr Anand Mohan Sur

 I first met Professor Anand Mohan Sur in 1977 when I was a third-year medical student. He was heading the department of Pediatrics of Government Medical College, Nagpur. Dr Sur took our class on basics in pediatrics. We students were spellbound by his talk. He was a forceful orator, to the point, precise, and had an extraordinary mastery over English literature. Later I had the opportunity to interact with him and found that he had mastery over Bengali literature too. He was very fond of Rabindra Sangeet and had translated a few songs of Tagore into Hindi.

Dr Sur was instrumental in developing pediatrics as an independent subject in medical curriculum. He argued that the neonates and children vary from adults in many ways. It is an art to diagnose an illness of a newborn, which a regular physician will not be able to do. A newborn, infant, or child does not complain, cannot express, and so only an expert can deal with them. The university accepted his arguments and thus pediatrics became a separate subject in MBBS curriculum.

He had an extensive research work and publications on Indian Childhood Cirrhosis (ICC). He proved that this is a different entity from common cirrhosis of liver and needs a different line of treatment. His paper was published in British Medical journal.

He was very popular not only among his students but also among his patients. His popularity could be gauged by the queue in the outdoor patient department of Government Medical College on his out-patient days. He did not care for the socio-economic status of patients and treated everyone equally. He developed the department of pediatrics of Medical College with untiring hard work and devotion.

Dr Sur was a voracious reader and was addicted to his passion for research and publication of papers in index journals.

A day prior to his ill-fated accident he was giving final touches to his scientific paper till late night. Next day he went to deliver a lecture for MBBS students at Lata Mangeshkar Hospital situated at Hingna. On the way back home, he met with an accident.

Dr Sur was full of compassion for all. One fine night I got a call from him that his dog had developed kidney failure and it was critically ill. Dr Sur had rushed the dog to a veterinary doctor who had given up all hopes. The dog had stopped passing urine and was comatose. Dr Sur wanted me to put the patient on dialysis. When I informed him that we have no machines, which could cater to dogs, he was demoralised. He frantically called various veterinary hospitals in India where dialysis could be done and found one at Chennai. He with his family took the dog in a van and drove to Chennai but alas, the dog died on the way. Later Dr Sur talked to me with tearful eyes that the dog had become his family member. For a long time, he felt its absence. Such was his compassion for animals.

With the demise of Dr Anand Mohan Sur, the medical fraternity of Nagpur has lost a great teacher and the people of Nagpur have lost a great pediatrician and excellent human being.

27.07.2007

# Dr Vijay Shrikhande
## A friend Indeed

 In the year 1989, when I started my practice in Nagpur, I needed a surgical colleague to help me in my uro-surgical cases. Though I had heard about Dr Vijay Shrikhande, I had never met him. So one fine evening, I walked into his chamber to introduce myself. He warmly welcomed me and the foundation of a strong and lasting friendship was laid. Later he presided over the inauguration of my hospital along with Dr B.J. Subhedar sir.

Dr Shrikande was a key member of the kidney transplantation team, which performed the first kidney transplantation in Central India in 1989. I remember vividly the feelings of apprehension, anxiety, nervousness, and excitement as we, Dr Shrikhande, Dr Joglekar, and I, set about this Herculean task of starting kidney transplantation in Nagpur. We searched for a hospital with a proper operation theatre, decided on the logistics, trained the nursing staff, and ultimately reached our goal of starting kidney transplantation in Central India. He was with me through the entire journey.

When Dr Shrikhande, Dr Joglekar, and I started our hospital together in Dhantoli, I saw another side of Dr Shrikhande. I saw how he handled disputes with the builder landowner with decisiveness and firmness. Almost seven years later we could move into the premises.

A great doctor and academician, Dr Shrikhande was the Chairman of Scientific Committee of the annual conference of Urology Society of India held in Nagpur in 2001 and what a scientific feast it was! He was also part of many awareness programmes in the Central India Kidney Foundation. The Central India Nephrology and Urology Societies jointly honoured him with the Lifetime Achievement Award in 2015.

I remember post-OPD chats with him -sometimes on difficult cases and sometimes on other hospital related issues. His gentle yet firm and no-nonsense approach to problems amazed me.

With his demise, Central India has lost a great son; his patients, a kind doctor with a magical touch; and me, a friend, philosopher, and guide.

We miss you dear friend.

4.08.2016

# Dr Arvind Joglekar - An Artistic Surgeon

My friend and senior surgeon of the town, Dr Arvind M. Joglekar is no more. It's hard to believe but a painful truth. He was the member of first kidney transplant surgery done at Mure Memorial Hospital way back in 1990 along with Dr S.S. Joshi, Dr Chandrashekhar Thatte, Dr Vijay Shrikhande, Dr Arvind Joshi, Dr Mashankar, Dr Hemant Sane, and myself. The patient was a young Engineering student, Zulfiquar Ali, whose mother donated the kidney. None of the local team members charged any fees.

Dr Joglekar was the first surgeon of this region to do arterio-venous fistula surgery, a surgery important for dialysis in patients with kidney failure.

Dr Joglekar was very simple, kind-hearted, and honest to the core. Surgery was his passion. His dissections were precise and textbook picture. Dr Joglekar, a professor of surgery in Indira Gandhi Medical College, Nagpur, was rated as one of the best teachers.

By nature, he was an artist. He would often sketch his surgical findings after the surgery was over. He used to help poor patients and did not charge them. Every year he used to go for free surgical camp conducted at Hemalkasa where tribal patients used to get operated free of charge.

Dr Joglekar was also passionate about wildlife and nature. Every two years during summer days he used to go for tiger census in nearby jungle. He would often go for tracking and for adventure in forests. This time he went to Bharatpur Bird Sanctuary.

In Dr Joglekar, we had a good human being and a surgeon par excellence. We shall miss him forever.

22.02.2019

# Dr Mukund Baheti – A Born Fighter

"The world's greatest achievers have been those who have always stayed focused on their goals and have been consistent in their efforts."

When a person is faced with all odds, when things look difficult and unachievable, through sheer determination, grit, and hard work, one can achieve their goal. Dr Mukund Baheti was one such person. To begin with, he had joined an *Ayuvedic* course. Later he did not only did MBBS and MD but did a super specialization in Neurology as well. He was an academic-oriented person.

Besides serving countless patients suffering from brain and spine related ailments, he also pursued teaching. For more than a decade he conducted free neurology classes for undergraduate and postgraduate medical students and practicing doctors under the aegis of Indian Medical Association.

He also guided *Ayurvedic* doctors on research methodologies.

"It is your brain, use it or lose it. Brain can be kept healthy only by keeping it active with daily activities like reading, problem solving etc.", he used to say.

I came close to Dr Baheti when he underwent kidney transplantation surgery as his kidneys failed due to diabetes. I was amazed to see the depth of his knowledge and analytical mind. During his illness he mastered the subject of Nephrology as well!

He continued to serve patients despite his health issues. He was a source of inspiration for his poor patients. He avoided costly investigations and used minimum medications.

We will remember him because he fought until the end; he was a true warrior, he never gave up, despite the debilitating ailments.

Goodbye dear friend!

06.01.2018

# Poems

# Desire

My heart
With endless wishes
Yearns for your sweet smile
Craves with umpteen desires
Gropes in the darkness
But as I look back in to my palms
It's all empty
And full of scratches
Droplets of dried blood
Stare at me.
Why did I desire
Why did I yearn
Then I get the answer
I am a mortal human
Desire germinates in my heart
Even if its a desert
Even if these shall dry and
Wither off
Desire
I MUST.

13.07.2016

# The Golden Girl

She knew not how to smile
Nor did she know how to catwalk
She had never applied fair and lovely,
Colour of her skin did never matter.

An apple of her father's eyes
And darling of her Maa
She ran for miles without shoes
With half-tummy-full of left over rice.

Had never asked for lollipops
Or yearned for dancing doll
No one had offered her ice cream
None wished her happy birthday
For she never knew what a birthday was!

She  fought with her dear brother
And always heartily lost the battle
But never did she lose the battle in real arena
Never did she leave the ground without fight.

She is our lovely daughter
Darling of millions
She did what the riches could not
Sweated &  sweated to reach her goal.

She is different
She did different
Never did she run after the crowd
Shattered the notion that
Lass are meant for kitchen.

Made her own trail
Danced to her own tune
Never bothered what her mates did
Simple as she is
Did what she liked
Did what she thought is right.

Ran for the Gold
Back with the Gold
Our this dark girl
Illumined the arena
With her golden heist.

Only they leave a mark
Who do not follow a trail but create one
Who do not give a damn
What others thought awry
Left the tradition to build one
Like our darling Hima Das.

Determined she shook the world
Star of today
'Dhing Express'
Our sweet Hima Das.

17.09.2018

*Background - Hima Das, the Asian Games 2018 medalist*

# For My Kids

Spread your wings without fear
Keeping aside pulls or pushes
Of near or dear

Yes
The world is bitterly harsh
Ready to dump you in to the trash

But world is equally beautiful
Ready to  offer  you sweet reward
If you sweat,
Struggle and
Sow seeds proper,
Thou shall reap rich,
Shall not turn pauper

Dark night is gifted with fresh sunlight
Storms followed by sweet breeze
Spring follows Bone chilling winter
Rains shower only after merciless summer

It all depends
On your foundation
If it's weak
It will crumble in pressure
As you pour your all into it

It lasts for generations
Like minaret Qutub
Stand tall without perturbation.

6.01.2018

# Path Unknown

We are travellers
We just walk
In a path unknown

At times we feel like
Master of our destiny
At times of other's too!!

As we age
Reality dawns over,
With lips tight
Frown of worries on forehead
Then we are called wise
While in the heart
We turn barren day by day

Then we yearn with earnest prayers
If those childhood days could come back...
If the tide of the time could reverse back
And needles of the clock could run backwards.

If we could go back
Like a child into lap of our beloved mother
If we could tightly hold the warm fingers of our Father
The way we had held on the first day of our school.
If we could again fight with our beloved sister

Now living in a distant land
Or play hide and seek with younger brother.

Alas
If I get back those days
I would just cling to these
Never to leave
Those tender spotless shiny truthful lovely childhood
moments.

Miss those who left long back
For anonymous retreat
Through this dusty path.

Someone inside me
Tells me to have faith
Have courage
Have patience
For
There is a purpose of our journey
In this path unknown.

6.1.18

# Thus Speaks My Heart

My heart speaks to me every moment

It's challenging
But worth taking the risk
Few more moments to live
Few more aspirations to fulfill
Life is so beautiful
Lovely is this journey
Loving are the people
Lovely is the company
Of charming friends like you

As I look back
It is worth being here in this mortal world
Some roses, some thorns
Some hot, some cold
Some easy, some arduous
Some hopes, few illusions
But every moment sprinkled by
His presence.

15.10.2016

# Adieu

The ever-strong time flies by
Like sand, it percolates out of our hands

Time! So cruel
So ruthless, so impatient
Could it not wait for a while?

Could it not wait for a little more?
To look more closely at our dear ones
Could we not have said -
Don't drop the curtains
For I am with my dear ones now!

When I see your tears
My eyes get wet,
As I see you smile
Flowers bloom in my heart,
As you shout with joy
My happiness knows no bound,
As you reach the sky
I feel the pride,
My friends
I love you
More than you ever thought.

Game is yet to be over
The knights and pawns have fallen
The King is yet to play its last move
The strings are yet to be pulled!

The party has just begun
Ecstatic dance on the floor
The wine is being served
Glasses are still not empty....

As we depart
My trembling nervous sweating palms
Try to hold on to you
"Do not leave, my friend"
Your aroma shall linger on
In this empty hall
Alas,
If I could hold these moments for eternity!


15.10.2018

Printed by Libri Plureos GmbH in Hamburg, Germany